LEGACY
OF
LIES

Over the Fence in Laos

Henry G. Gole

Cover and interior design: Jacqueline Cook

Author image courtesy of Matthew D. Morton

ISBN-13: 978-1-929932-41-2 Paperback
ISBN-10: 1-929932-41-3 Paperback

ISBN-13: 978-1-929932-42-9 eBook
ISBN-10: 1-929932-42-1 eBook

BISAC Subject Headings:
FIC002000 FICTION / Action & Adventure
FIC014000FICTION / Historical
FIC032000FICTION / War & Military

10 9 8 7 6 5 4 3 2 1

11715 Bandlon Drive,
Houston, TX 77072
Contact: golehg@aol.com

www.sogchronicles.com

Dedicated to Michael Gole, who served.

LEGACY
OF
LIES

Over the Fence in Laos

Henry G. Gole

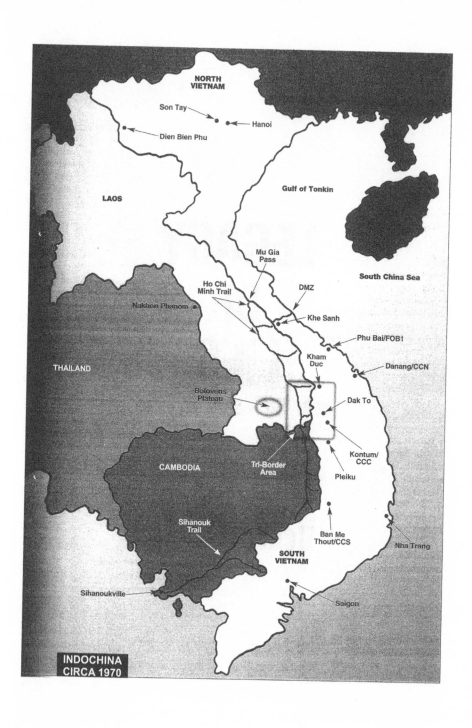

NORTH
VIETNAM

Son Tay
Hanoi

Dien Bien Phu

LAOS

Gulf of Tonkin

Mu Gia
Pass

Ho Chi
Minh Trail

DMZ

South China Sea

Nakhon Phanom

Khe Sanh

Phu Bai/FOB1

Kham
Duc

Danang/CCN

THAILAND

Bolovens
Plateau

Dak To

CAMBODIA

Kontum/
CCC

Tri-Border
Area

Pleiku

Sihanouk
Trail

Ban Me
Thout/CCS

Nha Trang

SOUTH
VIETNAM

Sihanoukville

Saigon

INDOCHINA
CIRCA 1970

Acknowledgments

I have been drafting, editing, and rewriting *Legacy of Lies* for about thirty-five years. I would be ungrateful if I did not at least state the names of trusted friends and colleagues who read drafts and commented about my efforts, some comments threatening friendship, some causing me to puff up my chest. The trend over the years has been from harsh criticism to praise, proving the validity of the old axiom: practice makes (not quite) perfect.

Wife Lydia Gole, with more than sixty years time-in-grade, marked up an early draft until it looked like a target successfully engaged by a Claymore mine. Keeping it in the family, skilled scribe and editor brother Bill Gole cleaned up a draft, not for the first time. Tony Nadal liked the action, but said my character development failed. Mark Hurley said my working title at the time, *The Blocking Force*, suggested the digestive problem of an aging man more than a daring military operation. Roger Spiller liked a later draft but proclaimed, "There's a novel in there somewhere. We need to find it." These and other honest comments forced me to practice what I preach: the secret to writing is rewriting. I rewrote.

My close pals from shared adventures in the bush were more forgiving, I think because I got the action right. Billy Boggs said it was just right the way I wrote it. Bill Roderick, after close analysis, said the same thing. (I suspected that friendship formed in the boonies softened critical blows that became pats on the back.) Roger Pezelle, my boss located in Saigon in 1970 when I was in CCC, a MACVSOG outfit in Kontum, had earlier served on the JCS staff in Washington. He liked my close combat actions and informed me how the pecking order from Washington to Saigon to Kontum worked. Kent Bolster's detailed interviews with SOG veterans fleshed out events that were sketchy in my mind. Rick Swain has always been in my corner as I scribbled nonfiction and now, fiction. Mary Stewart gave me a constructive critique and a bonus. She referred me to Jim Hanlon, a scrupulous editor who became more than an editor to me. Matt Morton noted the short distance from fact to fiction.

I knew I was in the homestretch when author Tom Ricks read an entire draft, provided wise advice, and praised it outrageously. Then, Steve Sherman showed it to Tom Yarborough, who is not only a published author of military books but also a retired United States Air Force colonel who piloted the small Forward Air Control (FAC) bird—we called it "Covey"—over Laos, quite literally the lifeline to our recon teams on the ground. Yarborough called it the best SOG book he has seen. (SOG is short for MACVSOG, the headquarters in Saigon. It means Studies and Observation Group, but many called it Special Operations Group, illustrating the need to be careful with cover names.)

So, my book was ready to go. But this first-time novelist didn't know how to get a *novel* published. And agents are not interested in geezer-scribes. Steve Sherman, a long-time chronicler of Special Forces, said: "Leave it to me." I did. He enlisted Faith Meyer Yeung, outstanding copy editor, and Jacquie Cook, who formatted my words by gently stirring them with electrons for eBook and print. I'd like to blame others for errors in *Legacy of Lies* and take a self-congratulatory bow, but that is bad form. Instead, I thank all named and some unnamed, and I accept responsibility for errors and shortcomings in my novel, a work of fiction based on my soldiering from 1952 to 1988.

Introduction

In 1988, just before I retired from active military duty, I got long-awaited access to the voluminous classified files of MACVSOG that were kept behind a green door in the bowels of the Pentagon. I thought I had struck gold. My 1970-71 tour with Command and Control Center (CCC), MACVSOG, in Kontum, convinced me that SOG was the story of unusually brave and skilled soldiers. If properly told, it would reflect great credit on the U. S. Army, at a time when its reputation was still that of the gang that couldn't shoot straight. I made my case to duly constituted (and misguided) authority and was denied. MACVSOG was still "classified" in 1988. No go.

Sensational bits and pieces about SOG leaked into print over the next decades. (We Americans are not good at keeping secrets.) Some of the yarns were quite good, but none of them were comprehensive. A thoroughly researched and carefully written history of SOG, the one I wanted to write in 1988, was needed.

I couldn't get the SOG men off my mind, so I wrote the story—in a mere 35 years—as fiction, allowing me to show gutsy soldiers on secret and dangerous missions in denied areas. Men I knew in Korea and in the 10th and 5th Special Forces Groups provided me with characters whose composites appear in my novel. Time in the bush and as intelligence and operations officer at the tactical level was followed by assignments to the Pentagon, an embassy, and the Army War College, allowing me to put tactical events in the field into the chain of command, from recon team leader to Kontum, Saigon, Honolulu, and Washington.

Secret missions require cover stories, deception, or, in plain English, lies. Lies have consequences, a legacy.

This is a work of fiction. The mission is my invention. Any similarity of characters and real persons is coincidental.

CHAPTER ONE

Fat Albert's Recon

Saigon, OP 35

U. S. Army colonels, like most government-issue equipment, come in various sizes, shapes and contents, normally olive drab in color. Colonel Roger Pietro was unremarkable in his average size and shape. The jungle fatigues he was wearing, more comfortable and functional than the versions he wore in two earlier wars, were still OD. He was a reasonably fit man, though in his late forties the bloom was off the rose. He had no particularly distinguishing physical characteristics, if one generously overlooked the receding hairline and thinning hair above his neat rimless glasses that gave him a professorial look. But he made no claim to high intelligence or intellectual power. In fact, his objective self-assessment was that he either brought up the rear of first-rate professionals, or he led the pack of second-raters. This was not false modesty. He was scrupulously honest.

Though Pietro made no such claim, and would probably deny it, he was remarkable for the optimal blend of what was in his head and heart. He had technical information and processes in his head, stuff learned in schools at Fort Benning, Fort Leavenworth, and Carlisle Barracks that was confirmed, denied and augmented by experience in the field. It ranged from tactics at the squad level to security policy and strategy at the national level. He knew staff work, the capabilities and limitations of weapons and, most significantly, he understood soldiers. He was surprised each time he encountered leaders who did not totally identify with their soldiers. That happened routinely in what he called the U.S. Army, Inc. And that is why he chose the fraternity of special operators, first OSS, later Special Forces.

Pietro was sound in his thinking and judgment, deliberate in speech, and clear in the orders he gave. Clarity made him confident, and confidence made him modest. Because he was modest—even self-effacing—and always courteous, he would have been surprised to hear that others considered this harmony of head and heart unique. Head plus profession made him a practical man; heart plus profession made him a hopeless romantic. This happy combination produced a leader with a firm grasp of the metrics of soldiering and Kipling-like affection for the poetry of soldiering. It told him what made elite soldiers tick. Forced into words, the skills and will of his soldiers met Pietro's essence in a way that gave him enormous gratification in what he did so well.

If he had a weakness—he would not call it that; he saw it as a reflex like breathing—it was that he cared too much for his soldiers. He called them his chickadees and worried about them constantly. He did verbalize clichés like, "we are all in this together," but that is precisely how he felt about what unified the cocky young studs in the field, his bright assistants in the headquarters, and his fellow old dogs up and down the chain of command from Da Nang, Kontum and Buon Ma Thuot to Saigon, Honolulu and Washington, D.C.

Pietro's lifelong affection for soldiers, most particularly for those who now dueled with a skilled enemy in Laos and Cambodia "up close and personal," was magnified by a simple fact: his son had been killed two years earlier while serving as a rifleman in a company of the 101st Airborne. The lad grew up an Army brat and wanted to have his war—that was here and now—before following a hazy scheme to go on to college on the GI Bill or to West Point, followed by some wonderful but indeterminate future in a big, wide, inviting world. Youthful plans came to an end in the A Shau valley, a very bad place where enemy skill and determination and unidentified strains of malaria and other diseases defied American efforts to prevail there for the entire duration of the war.

When Pietro mused about his son's death—unsolicited thoughts and memories irregularly broke into his consciousness daily—the old soldier confronted the irony: the old man comes through three wars with no more than a scratch or two; the lad never saw his twentieth birthday. Such musing flowed directly into concern for other lads, the three reconnaissance teams on current operations he had put in harm's way. The team in the DMZ between North Vietnam and South Vietnam had been pulled out, with no casualties, just hours ago. Another, inserted into Laos from Vietnam, made contact with the enemy upon insertion and was extracted, also without casualties.

That left the team led by an NCO, a comrade from the old days, in Laos north of the tri-border where Laos, Vietnam and Cambodia come together. We hadn't been able to get a team into that area for years, despite our best efforts to do so. How the team from Kontum managed to get in and stay in undetected for two days was both noteworthy and a cause of concern by the old Colonel. The team leader's extraordinary field expertise was matched by wit and humor best described as whimsical. He called himself Fat Albert.

Laos

Hahn, a big blond man, was scared.

He gasped for air as much from fear as from physical exertion. Every cell in his body was on full alert, ready for fight or flight. He concentrated on not trembling.

Fat Albert, leader of Reconnaissance Team Alabama, Hahn, and the four Montagnards on this mission had heard the North Vietnamese trackers on their back trail some five or ten minutes earlier. It was obvious to the experienced recon men that the team was being followed. In the past couple of minutes, their pursuers—about 100 meters behind them—had started thrashing about and shouting, confident that their strength was sufficient to run down and overpower the intruders. Fat Albert's team was on their turf, a previously unidentified north-south infiltration route hidden in the dense jungles of eastern Laos.

RT Alabama was on its own, at least fifty miles from the nearest friendly faces, most of them brown, at a Special Forces border camp in Vietnam. Their skills and luck—at times like this it was difficult to know which was more important—would decide between life and death.

Frequent battle drills, and the fact that Bob Hahn had been Fat Albert's number two man for a half-dozen missions into Laos in the previous eight months, made protracted conversation unnecessary. His assessment complete, the team leader turned to Hahn: "Contact Covey for extraction. Five hundred meters and wait." He pointed in the direction intended. Hahn shot an azimuth on his compass in the direction indicated. He would guide his point man on that azimuth. Without comment, Hahn started moving, taking with him three of the small men. One positioned himself in front of the American and moved in the direction Hahn pointed. Two fell in behind them. As they moved out, Hahn pressed the "push to talk" button on his radio to contact a guardian angel.

"Covey, this is Alabama One-One."

Fat Albert observed their departure, confident that Sergeant Hahn would coordinate the extraction of the team and lead the RT to a place where a helicopter could either land or hover over ropes dropped to the men on the ground. He intended to follow Hahn's trail after slowing the pursuers.

Being a recon team leader—the "One-Zero" in the lexicon of recon men—meant that Fat Albert called the shots and took the short end of the stick in crunch time. Always. In all of his battle drills, he was at the critical point so that he could quickly assess the actual situation. He accepted the inherent risks in order to make timely decisions. That's why he was still alive after almost a hundred missions "over the fence" into Laos and Cambodia from both South Vietnam and Thailand. That was also the reason the members of RT Alabama never hesitated to execute when Fat Albert spoke. Explanations and discussions were for later, at the mission debriefing in Kontum and still later over a beer as they decompressed.

In the immediate situation he provided rear security as Hahn contacted Covey, a small fixed wing aircraft that was the link between the team on the ground and the aerial circus supporting the team. Hahn could handle the extraction, but he needed a little time. Fat Albert would buy that time.

***

The aircraft piloted by a U.S. Air Force captain was out of sight of Alabama—more significantly, out of sight of the team's pursuers—but a radio transmission from the RT would bring Covey on the scene in a flash. That was its reason for being. Next to the captain was a Special Forces sergeant, himself a former RT leader, a One-Zero, with a dozen missions on the ground behind him and two years of flying Covey. Between the two men there was an unwritten contract more binding than any formal piece of paper: when the recon teams were in trouble, these two men would do anything to support them or get them out. Anything.

No one knew the Area of Operations, the AO, as well as the Covey crews. A half-dozen Air Force pilots from Pleiku and four Special Forces NCOs from the camp in Kontum flew the clandestine missions. They knew the territory, the capabilities and limitations of the various teams on the ground, and the components of the support immediately available and responsive to their call: troop-transporting "slicks" to insert and extract teams, and fire support from Cobra helicopters, air force jet aircraft, and the big, slow, propeller-driven World War II vintage A-1 Skyraider.

Recon men and Covey were keenly aware that the trick was to know precisely what the various birds could do and to use air assets with great care. The bombs, rockets, machine guns, napalm and cannons didn't know the difference between the man from Hartford and the man from Hanoi. Further, the enemy was a quick read: He learned early on that he was safer belly to belly with a recon team of four to a dozen

15

lightly armed men than he was standing off a hundred meters or more, a target of American air power.

Alabama had initiated direct action just before the previous day. It was not planned. The team's job was to observe and report, but they had stumbled upon two armed trail watchers just as Fat Albert was selecting his overnight hide position for the team. They killed the pair, and then had moved for an hour before going to ground for the night in a thicket well off any known trail. At first light the trackers had probably found their dead soldiers and picked up the team's trail to where they were playing out the hand. Now Fat Albert and the Montagnard two meters from him, Baby-San, had a simple task: slow the trackers with the means at hand—automatic rifles, hand grenades, Claymore mines, and their wits.

A few minutes was all the RT would need to put some distance between it and the pursuers. The moderately thick jungle limited visibility on the ground to generally five or ten meters, but even in such vegetation there were lanes providing visibility out to some twenty or thirty meters. Fat Albert and Baby-San overlooked such a lane. This cat and mouse game was not new to them. Hunters and hunted reversed roles often as the game played out. Baby-San had over thirty missions with his leader and trusted him completely. He concentrated on the immediate and reacted to his One-Zero instantly and trustingly.

A 100 meter head start would allow the team to get out of harm's way, out of the jungle, out of Laos, and back to a hot meal, a warm shower, a cold beer, and the customary all-night wind-down bull session. Then they'd settle into their first real sleep in four days. At 100 meters, maybe 50, the pursuers would hear what was happening to the front, but they would not be able to take aimed shots at the team or the extraction bird. The best way to buy those minutes and meters for the RT was to inflict casualties on the trackers to slow them.

Fat Albert considered a Claymore mine ambush but decided against it. That low risk option had the big advantage of not revealing his exact position, but the pursuers would have to walk into the relatively small killing zone of the Claymore. This was unlikely, since the enemy knew the RT was in the area. These North Vietnamese soldiers were specialists brought to this place in Laos to run down the American-led teams and kill them. The enemy had lost enough people in this deadly game to realize that only his first team could run down the other guy's first team. Losers didn't get to play next week.

He gave the enemy full credit. Good troops would smell a rat in this patch where the terrain opened up just a tad. Although he generally avoided direct action, Fat Albert reluctantly concluded that he and Baby-San would have to drop one or two trackers with fire if the pursuers were to be slowed. A firefight, even when an RT gets the drop on the enemy, usually means the end of their mission: picking up intelligence information. At the moment he had important information for the intelligence officer at Kontum. His task was to deliver it, not to win the war in that part of Laos.

Engaging the enemy with his individual weapon would reveal his position. So be it. That was the best course of action available. There was some consolation in knowing that Hahn also had the critical and actionable information in his grubby notebook.

***

Hahn was startled at the sudden sound of automatic weapons fire from Fat Albert's position, back where the team had split into two elements. Even though he had been waiting for the sound of close combat, the exchange of AK-47 and CAR-15 fire jangled his nerves. The reason was not immediately apparent to him.

Hahn had told Covey to get ready for a "hot extraction" of Alabama. Actually, Hahn said, "Hank Snow, Red!" That was an unofficial brevity code. It told the aircraft drivers descending toward an opaque green-on-green carpet that concealed the tense scene below the triple canopy, "We want out, now!" The reference to Hank Snow was actually to one of his hit songs known to shit-kickers, "Movin' On." The official code for immediate extraction was to declare Prairie Fire. That resulted in absolute priority by higher headquarters to get the team out. But Fat Albert had an aversion to admitting to a desperate situation. He and Hahn had done the impossible routinely. Besides, he liked Hank Snow.

Covey clearly understood the situation and had ordered up a slick chopper to carry the team to safety, a pair of gunships to cover the slick, and a second slick called "the chase bird" as insurance. Recon men liked the machine gun fire and rockets Cobras could put on targets up close and personal. Each of the 70 or so rockets was packed with dart-like projectiles that the recon men called "nails." Teams had great confidence in the gunships and used their fire even when in close combat with the enemy. But gunships were choppers. They had to be used right away. Loiter time on target for helicopters was only ten to twenty minutes after the flight from Vietnam.

The "package" of four birds had been on strip alert at Dak To, a forward launch site in Vietnam close to the Laotian frontier. That meant they were prepared to be airborne as soon as Covey gave the word. Flight time to where they were needed was about twenty minutes. They had been underway for about fifteen minutes, the time it had taken Hahn and his three Montagnards to move in the direction of a landing zone.

The limited stay time of the gun ships meant that Alabama would use 'em quickly or lose 'em. Covey also launched a pair of A-1 Skyraiders from Pleiku. They would arrive on the scene about the time the helicopter gunships returned to Dak To for refueling and rearming.

Sergeant Carpenter, the Covey rider, gave Hahn a new azimuth to reach the landing zone designated for the extraction, some 1000 meters from Hahn's current position. At that distance was an LZ big enough for a one-bird extraction, and one bird could handle the combat-loaded weight of two Americans and four Yards. No sweat to take out one American and three Yards. But the new azimuth had an option built in for which Hahn would be grateful. About 400 meters along the new axis was a hole in the jungle canopy over which a chopper could hover, drop "strings," and lift out the team as an external load. Carpenter had spotted that option as insurance. He knew his job.

***

Hahn was reviewing the bidding in his head when the firefight erupted: Covey on station; guns and slicks underway; azimuth 130; 1000 to LZ; 400 to "string" extract; all-around security; his own CAR-

15 on automatic; ammo pocket for magazines open; ammo pocket to grenades open; smoke grenade ready to be popped. He figured that Fat Albert would soon detonate a Claymore to slow the trackers.

Then it hit him. The AKs had fired first! The AKs had initiated the contact! The enemy trackers had gotten the drop on Fat Albert and Baby-San. But the CAR-15s, clearly two of them, had returned fire. There was more firing of both types of weapons; then silence. Hahn told Covey what was happening.

"Covey, Bama One-One."

"Go, One-One."

"My One-Zero plus one in contact with trackers. I'm moving to my One-Zero on the last back azimuth. For sure I'll need nails."

"You call; we haul. Over."

"Rog. One-One. Out."

Hahn headed for a clearing and a slope he recalled seeing some hundred yards in the direction from which he had just come. From the top of the slope—it wasn't much, but it was the dominating terrain in the immediate neighborhood—he could cover the two men now making their way to the main body of the team, if four men could be called a main body. Once together again he would give Fat Albert the new azimuth and lead the team to the LZ.

He and the three Yards returned on the trail they had made. They paused at the clearing. He had lost all sense of time, and it seemed forever as he strained his eyes to find his friends in the thick jungle beyond the clearing.

***

A figure staggered into view. Shit! Fat Albert was carrying Baby-San piggyback! Hahn stood and waved both arms. Fat Albert squatted, gently lowered Baby-San to the ground, deliberately faced Hahn, and waved Hahn back. They were only twenty meters apart, but Hahn thought there was a misunderstanding as he again beckoned Fat Albert to join him. Baby-San was alive. As Hahn watched, he saw Baby-San face the direction of the trackers, elevating his weapon to his shoulder.

Fat Albert turned to face Hahn, gripping his CAR-15 with both hands. With the weapon parallel to the ground, Albert raised it over his head. In their battle drills this meant, "Look, you dumb shit! Give me your undivided attention." Then he pointed distinctly toward Hahn and then vigorously toward the LZ. He completed this dumb talk by making a fist and pumping it up and down, the standard military hand and arm signal for double-time. Haul ass!

Fat Albert had spoken. Hahn waved his three troopers back toward the LZ, conflicted but absolutely sure that he had been ordered to shag ass.

As they passed the point a hundred yards away where they had earlier waited for the rear guard, a short, intense firefight ensued behind them. This time the CAR-15s spoke first, but the AKs spoke last. Then there was a pause. Then two single shots rang out.

Hahn's first impulse was to go back to assist, but Fat Albert's last order was to get what was left of Alabama to safety and to get important info to Kontum. As he waved his point man toward the LZ, he had already made up his mind to go for the string extraction. It was closer; the bird would not have to expose itself completely to small arms fire; the RT would not have to enter a large clearing; the trackers wouldn't see their targets. He called Covey while on the move, panting from fear and fatigue, and followed his point man.

"Covey, One-One," he gasped as he fought the bush and talked.

"Go," said Carpenter.

"Moving to string extract. Four pax." Hahn almost sobbed as he added: "Fat Albert and one Yard probable KIA. Trackers 100 meters behind us."

"Rog. Do you want nails on your back trail?"

"Affirm. I'll pop smoke and move to strings. Give me zero two. Then talk to me and put nails on smoke."

The plan was made. Noting the break in the tree canopy directly above him and the absence of wind, Hahn dropped a smoke grenade at his feet. That was important. Often an excited trooper would activate a smoke grenade so that the smoke drifted under triple canopy foliage until it found breaks in the canopy that allowed it to rise. Those breaks might be hundreds of yards away, possibly over friendly troops.

Without a confirmed fix on the team, aerial observers had only the most general idea of the location of the friendlies and thus hesitated to work air-delivered ordnance too close to friendlies for fear of hitting the good guys.

Hahn dropped a green smoke grenade, leaving identification of color to Covey. Announcing the color before Covey confirmed it would invite every English speaking bad guy in Laos to toss a green smoke grenade to confuse American pilots providing air support.

The team was moving quickly toward the extraction point when Covey said, "I got green."

"Rog. Work from green on my back trail."

"Will work nails on your back trail from smoke. I estimate you are one five to extract point."

Covey was straining two pairs of eyes, trying to see the drama playing under the green roof, but failing. Carpenter could imagine it. He had been there.

The enemy knew that RT Alabama was running for its life and wanted to close with and destroy the team. But the hunted were also hunters who could respond with mines, grenades, automatic weapons and a little help from their friends.

***

It was difficult enough to navigate in the jungle without being in the high adventure mode caused by having bad guys on his ass. Hahn knew that gunships worked in pairs with a high bird covering and observing the low bird. He heard the lower gunship as it approached from his twelve o'clock toward his six o'clock, thus confirming that the aircraft was moving precisely on the azimuth Covey had given him. Just as it passed over the RT, the low bird fired its rockets at Hahn's green smoke and beyond.

"Covey, Cobra was directly above me when he released his nails." After a brief pause, Covey responded:

"Roger, One-One. He hosed your last smoke. I have a good fix on your location. You are two zero zero meters from string extract point. Pop smoke when you have hole in canopy. Gimme a panel at extract site. I have a slick in orbit."

The lives of the RT and the helicopter crew were in the hands of Sergeant Carpenter, the Covey rider choreographing the dance of death. He needed positive identification of Alabama before directing the slick to the hole in the jungle roof. Since the uniforms of NVA and friendly troops were designed to blend into the jungle in color and texture, it was easy to confuse friend and foe. Except for one blond American, both sides consisted of local boys.

"Covey, I got a hole. I popped smoke."

After a half minute Covey said:

"I got red."

"Roger. Red."

Again Hahn heard a gun ship approaching at high speed from straight ahead, and again he heard the welcome sound of the rockets being fired as the Cobra passed overhead and behind the RT. Suddenly he found himself in a part of the jungle that wasn't quite a clearing, but the vegetation was sparser than it had been moments earlier. He looked up and saw the sky. This was the place Covey had spotted from the air for a string extraction. He signaled the point man to halt, gave the rotating hand signal for all-around security, and pulled the bright panel from his rucksack. Looking up at the hole in the canopy, he put the panel on the ground with the bright orange color up.

"Covey, One-One. Bingo."

Carpenter strained his eyes searching for the panel, spotted it and told Hahn:

"Gotcha. I see orange."

"Affirm. Orange."

"I'll get slick on this freq. Wait."

Carpenter, like most experienced combat men, held the enemy in very high regard for courage and skill. He had played tag with them often in the jungle and from the sky.

"Brave little fuckers," he mused genteelly as he organized his assets to kill them.

During extraction he wanted the slick and Alabama to be in direct commo. Communications discipline was critical to success during an operation. Carpenter had been known to do physical harm to people for being dumb or verbose on the radio when he caught up to them, usually in a bar. His rule was simple: Covey called the shots. Be clear. Be brief.

He told the slick to switch to Alabama's primary frequency, one of several radio channels monitored by aircraft supporting the team on the ground.

"Sweet Sue One, go to Alabama's primary frequency."

"Wilco."

Sweet Sue One, the troop-carrying slick, was in direct voice communication with Hahn. Carpenter monitored that conversation while he spoke on another to the gunships.

"Red Baron Six, Covey."

"Go, Covey."

"Did you monitor Alabama and mine to Sweet Sue?"

"Rog. I have nails and beaucoup guns. You call."

"Use nails first from orange panel on azimuth you were working. Then use guns. Say when dry. Then I'll go to Skyraiders. Do you see panel?"

There was a momentary delay that seemed much longer. Then:

"Wilco. Nails first, then guns. I got negative visual on panel."

At this point the Cobra flying wingman with Red Baron Six broke in to report good news.

"Break, break. Six and Covey, this is Red Baron Four. I saw panel on last pass. I have firm fix on it."

"Four, this is Six. Roger. I take high position. You make a pass. Give me a 'Bingo' when you are over Alabama. Use nails first. Safe side one zero zero from panel until Alabama calls for closer."

Carpenter was a happy man as he surveyed the entire scene. Here he was, CINCFUWORLD, Commander-in-Chief-of-the-Fucking-World. The panel was visible to him and the gunships, which were shooting up Alabama's back trail. The slick was talking to Hahn. He had monitored Red Baron and was heading for the hover position over the team. The chase slick, flying orbit around the whole scene was prepared to pick up broken people and things if something fell out of the sky. I'm the leader of the band, he noted approvingly. On the internal net heard only by his pilot, he broke into his hymn of celebration: I got the whole world in my hand. He smiled contentedly. He had served with Fat Albert in Bad Tölz, Fort Bragg and Kontum. They weren't close, but there was professional respect between them. Carpenter figured that Fat Albert was one of the best of the recon men. With a little luck they might have a drink together tonight.

***

Hahn heard Covey, and he heard the slicks and guns. He moved to his three Montagnards, tapping each on the butt in turn. "One," he said to the first, holding up one finger in the Yard's face and pushing him straight ahead. To the next one he said, "Two," as he held up two fingers and pushed the man to the right, and "Three," as he pushed the last one to the left. Then Hahn did what he had so often seen Fat Albert do. He took up rear security in the direction of the enemy. Demand much of your troops. Then get them out in one piece. Hahn would be the last to hook up.

After a sweeping glance to his front, Hahn pushed the button on his radio handset: "Sweet Sue. Execute."

The slick hovered over the gap in the green roof and dropped two ropes, one from each door of the chopper. On each of the two "strings" were two loops close together and some thirty feet below the bird. One by one, the Yards grabbed the strings, pulled them down and snapped into the loops with the D-rings that were sewn into their load bearing harnesses.

Voices on the radio were added to the din of the gunship fire keeping the trackers off Alabama and the audible strain of the chopper hovering at treetop under full power. The guns poured rockets and then machine-gun fire 100 meters from the team, then at 50, and finally at 25 meters. Repeated passes and definite sightings of friend and foe allowed the pilots to support the RT confident that good guys were safe and bad guys were dying. As the Cobras broke clear and headed for the border, Hahn heard bombs falling two- or three- hundred meters on his back trail. That meant that Covey was working the A-1s. The enemy reinforcements rushing to kill or capture the Americans found themselves in a killing zone. Hahn saw his number three man flashing a thumbs-up and grinning.

Facing the direction from which an enemy approach was most likely, Hahn backed toward his three soldiers, and then turned for the last few steps as he slung his CAR-15 from the back of his neck so that the weapon rested on the ammo pockets on the front of his belt, freeing his hands. His number three grabbed the D-ring with one hand, hooked it into the loop in the string that he held with his other hand, and whacked Hahn on the butt shouting, "One-One OK!" Hahn then looked up to the rigger in the door of the chopper and gave a salute, the signal to lift up, clear the suspended troops from the jungle and haul ass. The slick pilot carefully ascended under full power until his human external cargo cleared the jungle. Then he flew like a bat out of hell away from the known location of the enemy.

The trip to Vietnam would be made with Hahn and the Yards dangling beneath the slick, just above tree top level. The method, called "contouring," was premised on the probability that the bird would buzz over any enemy in the forest so quickly that it would be gone before a surprised enemy could react with aimed fire.

Hahn settled into the ride. Increasingly in the next twenty minutes all feeling in his legs would first fade, to be replaced by throbbing pain as the leg straps bit into his upper legs. Then the sweat would begin to evaporate at 100 plus knots per hour, causing painful chilling. He felt good about getting the remnants of the team out of a tight spot. He felt good about the flying circus that had, not for the first time, saved his life. He thought of Fat Albert.

And he cried.

Grady Goes Home

Sergeant Kevin Grady returned from his free thirty-day leave, marking his second voluntary extension of duty in Vietnam. Lifting off from Travis Air Base, Grady nodded good-bye to the USA from his window seat and fitted himself into a space designed for about two-thirds of him. Flight time, twenty hours; total elapsed time, about thirty, long enough to turn his starched tan uniform soggy and to scuff his spit-shined jump boots. Every seat was stuffed with a soldier, most of them "cherries" going to war for the first time. Grady's previous flights had been Alaska, Japan, Okinawa and into Vietnam, or Hawaii to some speck of sand before a short stop at Okinawa and the last leg to Vietnam. Routing didn't matter. He was a package to be delivered. He would become a person again in Kontum.

No booze. He wasn't a boozer, but booze assured sleep for most of the flight over most of the Pacific. Sober, he dozed fitfully, squirmed, and awakened disheveled with a bad taste in his mouth.

Sensing final approach for a landing in the changed pitch of the big engines, he opened one eye, checked his watch, and tuned in. Aloha. Coffee. Mill around. Get back on the bird for more tedium.

The young soldier sitting next to Grady saw the gold medallion on a thick gold chain around his neck that peeked through his shirt.

"Jeez, Sarge, is that real gold?"

"It is."

"Can I see it?"

Grady pulled the chain and medallion over his head and passed them to his neighbor.

"FUCK COMMUNISM. Right, but what's this?"

The rookie pointed to the strange script on the reverse side of the medallion.

"It says, 'Congratulations, brave soldier. Good health and long life.' In Vietnamese."

The young soldier tested the weight.

"Heavy. What's is worth?"

"It cost me a thousand dollars."

"Wow! What's the idea?"

"The enemy who kills me gets a prize. In his world it's worth a fortune."

Handing back the gold, "Why give a prize to the guy who kills you?"

Grady replaced the gold, turned to the window, closed his eyes, and said, "Respect."

***

Doze. Squirm. Tasteless meal. Land. A glance down startles. About to dip wheels in water, the runway is suddenly there. Midway. Exit. Stretch. Coffee. Refuel. Board. Doze. Squirm. Land. Coffee. Bad taste. Okinawa is a big island. Next, Vietnam. His head is already there.

The door opened. Vietnam entered: too hot, too humid, too bright. His body rejoined his head.

New troops boarded buses with mesh wire covering windows, destined for a replacement center for more mill-around. But an NCO under a green beret smiled, read his name tag, and reached out a hand, saying:

"I'm your ride to B-55. Welcome home."

***

Grady spent the night in the safe house to enjoy a meal, a couple of beers and refreshing sleep. He was back at the airport the next day for the short flight to Kontum on an Air Force C-130. His nap on the cool metal floor of the aircraft ended with the bird's steep descent. Arriving aircraft were sometimes welcomed with rockets or mortars on the runway; therefore, rapid descent and brief engines-on. Before the bird halted, the flight chief kicked out cargo, which rolled un-assed down the conveyor belt on the now-lowered tailgate. Engine rpm built with a roar. The tailgate closed. Brakes released. The big bird raced down the runway trailing vortices of red dust. Total time on the ground was a minute or two, enough for flight pay and combat pay. Grady relaxed in the jeep seat for the short ride to CCC. The dust returned to the runway. The C-130 became a speck in the sky. He was back with his friends.

CHAPTER TWO

RT Alabama Debrief

Kontum

"Sir, Alabama ETA one-five on the pad."

Translation: RT Alabama will be here on the helicopter pad in about fifteen minutes.

Lieutenant Colonel Radich, the Command and Control Center (CCC) commander, acknowledged the report. He routinely met returning teams but didn't attend debriefings, believing that his presence inhibited the process. Nobody likes to have the boss breathing down his neck. Debriefs worked better NCO-to-NCO.

But this one was special. The "missing" team leader and Radich had shared earlier adventures in Asia. And Fat Albert was probably dead. Radich thought about the last commanders' meeting in Saigon with his boss, Colonel Pietro, and the officers commanding the other two land elements of the clandestine Studies and Observation Group. Little good news surfaced.

Command and Control North (CCN) in Da Nang was having a

hell of a time getting teams into northern Laos, and getting into the DMZ was a bitch. It was easier in '64, '65 and '66, before the enemy got smart about countering helicopter insertions and extractions. Now the North Vietnamese Army had almost all potential landing zones under observation. Increasingly, choppers were shot down or hit, or enemy hunter-killer teams pursued RTs from their insertion. Running ground recon into Laos from CCN was near suicidal.

Command and Control South (CCS) was in limbo. The president had directed termination of all U.S. combat operations in Cambodia. Colonel Pietro and his commander, who ran the whole SOG shooting match—land, air, sea, psy ops, agents—didn't know if the no-go was temporary or permanent. So, CCS had to wait with its finger up its ass, and CCN couldn't keep teams on the ground more than a few minutes. Helluva deal.

"That left us," Radich thought. "We could get into southern Laos. Sometimes. Fat Albert had gotten in and stayed in an area that had been impenetrable. Before Alabama's success, we lost four KIA and a dozen wounded trying a half-dozen times in the last year. Stay-time was measured in minutes, but Alabama lasted days. How'd he do it? What's in there that's so important to the enemy? A headquarters? Field hospital?"

Radich would attend the debriefing.

Master Sergeant Ken Key pushed open the wooden ammunition box cover that served as a door to Major Day's "office" in the bunker housing CCC's Tactical Operations Center. His boss, formally the Director of Operations and Intelligence, was variously known around the camp as the Mad Major or CINCTOC, an example of GI humor that made him Commander in Chief of the Tactical Operations Center. Ken smiled when he was with the Major and when he thought about him.

"Alabama's is zero five out, Major."

"OK, Ken. Let's go."

As they walked the 300 meters to the pad, Ken noticed that the Major was deep in thought. That usually meant something offbeat.

"Ya gonna tell me about it, sir?"

"I think we do some things right."

Key took his cue. The two of them took care of the hot stuff on the front burner, but when the Major ruminated aloud, as he often did, Key enjoyed their moments together. Ken spoke.

"Our guys do a good job in target prep for the RTs. They break their ass to get all the intel about the target. The recon guys trust them. And we do good debriefs."

"True. Target prep and debriefs are fine. I was thinking about the brief-back. You've been SF so long you may not realize that the brief-back is unique to us. We do that right. Maybe the rest of the Army could do it."

Ken paused and pondered. Like many SF troopers, Ken had cut his teeth in the airborne infantry.

"Dunno. We have time. Our guys are experienced. In the infantry it's usually one damn thing after the other without time to really think and plan. Squads and platoons don't have the time or experience to be part of planning. So the staff just tells the line outfits, mostly kids, 'Do it!'"

The Major nodded agreement. Ken was probably right. When SF soldiers were given a mission, they were given latitude in how they would do it. The Major told the recon team leader, the One-Zero, the outcome desired.

Get me a prisoner from this area.

Tap this wire.

Ambush there.

Observe this river. Say what traffic.

Conduct a linear recon from-to, noting trails crossed and possible LZs.

The One-Zero thought about the mission, asked questions, got answers, and came up with a concept. Then he submitted an equipment list, requests for photos and over-flights, and whatever he thought he needed. Then, he decided how many and who would go. He rehearsed his people. He developed a final plan.

Then he briefed his plan to the commander and his staff. They asked questions. The commander approved or modified the plan. The last question from the commander was always: Is there anything you need and didn't get?

Woe to the staffer who failed to give the operators what they needed!

Good system. Everybody is in the picture. We know what we want to do and who is responsible.

Ken and the Major's ruminations were interrupted by the distinctive pop-pop-pop of the HU1D helicopter—pronounced yew-ee.

***

Radich was at the debriefing along with Major Day, the Recon Company First Sergeant, and the Recon Company Commander.

Key conducted the debriefing. Another intel sergeant took notes. Key was the target NCO for Alabama, the man who did the research for the team, briefed the RT, got the info and materials the One-Zero needed. He was involved from initial concept to after action report.

The two to four hour session was informal in tone and highly stylized in language. The product was precise and unembellished. Blandness was the model of ideal military communication: clear, concise, and complete. Struggles at a primitive level were "contacts." Pain, terror, and loss of legs became "WIA was not ambulatory." Activating a mine that shredded human bodies was "successful ambush at coordinates BS12345678." The chaos of noise, fear, and confusion were rendered as: "RT extracted from LZ under ground fire. Aircraft took hits."

A format designed to miss nothing guided the debriefing. Much of the after action report—the AAR—was already done. Before departing Kontum, the leader had noted in writing: when he got the warning order; the intelligence provided on the enemy, the terrain and the weather; team preparation, to include training, requests for equipment and support from the various staff sections, and their responses; the mission; and the leader's plan to accomplish the mission. Team members were listed by name; everything each man carried on the mission was listed. Sergeant Key already had all of this.

Copies of all journal entries, communications, and reports from the Launch Officer in Kontum, the Forward Operating Base at Dak To, and the commo section were given to the debriefer as soon as practicable. Situation Reports—SITREPS—sent by Alabama during the mission were on file as were relevant messages from aerial observers. Even in an army infamous for collecting the most bits and pieces of paper since the demise of the Third Reich, Key heard no complaints about this method designed to assure that the RT survived and got the job done. No one objected to either.

Four copies of the AAR, some twenty to thirty pages each, were made. One went to Joint Special Ops Activities, Joint Chiefs of Staff, the Pentagon (JSOA in military jargon); one to Commander-in-Chief, Pacific (CINCPAC) in Honolulu; one to SOG headquarters in Saigon; and a copy was kept in Kontum for a year before it was destroyed.

A précis of the report would be telexed to Washington, Honolulu, and Saigon within 24 hours of team extraction. The RT debrief completed the picture.

***

Key read aloud the mission statement and outlined Fat Albert's plan to accomplish it. Hahn interrupted.

"Did Carpenter contact Albert?"

"Negative. Carpenter is still in the AO."

Key paused to allow Hahn to come to terms with the loss of his friend. Everyone in camp and in the chain of command from Saigon to Washington wanted to know if there was a chance that Fat Albert was alive and on the run. Covey coverage would be constant with one aircraft relieving the other on station.

Key softened his voice.

"Let's review what happened and the last time you saw Albert."

"I shoulda stayed."

Hahn was on the verge of tears. Key understood. Feeling guilt is common among survivors. They believe they should have done more for those who didn't make it. Guilt was compounded by the respect and affection Hahn had for his friend, leader, and mentor. Others could commiserate, explain, but Hahn knew he was alive and Albert probably wasn't. After the debriefing he'd eat steak, fresh bread, pineapple, drink a few beers, and probably seek feminine companionship with some belle from the ville. Albert was dead. Or worse.

"The four of us coulda gone back and helped Albert with Baby-San. We'd all be here now."

Or none, thought Key. But he said:

"Pick it up with first light today: six Alabama men in the overnight position. What happened?"

"We heard trackers on our back trail. Albert sent me toward an LZ. He and Baby-San covered our back trail."

Hahn went on in a monotone until he described Albert carrying the wounded Yard piggyback, lowering him, and emphatically motioning Hahn to the LZ. He choked up. So did the others. They saw Albert choosing death with Baby-San over life as a leader who left a wounded member of his team to the enemy. Hahn tried to compose himself. The room was still as each man in the room, all veterans of close combat, painted his own picture of Fat Albert and thought the team leader's thoughts.

Radich had a nice touch with his roughnecks and a special place in his heart for the brave men who let it all hang out. He also knew his business. He had spent almost twenty years in Vietnam, Taiwan, Thailand, and Korea and on mobile training team missions sent from home base in Okinawa to almost every corner of the Far East. His marriage was in trouble because he extended his tour in Vietnam to take command of CCC, the best assignment of what he regarded as a fine career.

He had known Fat Albert for years—much longer than Hahn knew Albert—in Fort Bragg, Okinawa, Thailand, and in several tours in Cambodia and Vietnam. Everyone in the room knew that. Key had known both men in the various assignments in Asia. Albert and Radich had attended Key's marriage to an Okinawan girl twelve years earlier. They were friends. Hahn knew none of that.

Radich put his hand on the younger man's shoulder.

"Bob, what did Albert intend with the high rifle signal."

"Sir, that meant haul ass."

"And when he pointed?"

"The direction he wanted me to go."

"How many times did he give you that signal in your quick reaction drills, in training and on ops?"

"Sir, hundreds of times."

"Say again the last voice communication you had with him."

"He said 'contact Covey for extraction. Go five hundred meters in the direction he pointed. Wait there.'"

"Did you do that?"

"Yes, sir."

"Did you do exactly that?"

"Yes, sir."

"The next order was the rifle signal?"

"Yes, sir."

Radich paused for a long time. Everyone but Hahn saw exactly what the Old Man was doing and loved him for it. He patted Hahn's shoulder, looked him in the eye with their faces a foot apart, and said:

"You did an outstanding job. You got out the three men Albert put in your hands. Carpenter said the string extraction was textbook. Smooth as goose shit. Albert trained you. You obeyed his clear orders, because he trained you to do that. You did the right thing. So did Albert."

Again there was a long pause as he let the words sink in. Then he said:

"It's right to feel bad and to shed a tear for a great soldier. You did exactly what Albert wanted you to do. You done good."

Radich restored Hahn's honor in Hahn's eyes and made Albert the selfless hero he was. That made it easier to accept what happened.

***

Alabama's mission was a classic linear recon from a specific point to a specific point. The object was to confirm or deny the existence of an alternate route to the known north-to-south enemy main supply route. Measurements, precise locations, and photos of the alternate trails, if any, would be brought back to Kontum to be sent up the chain of command in the AAR.

The mission had been requested by the Air Force intelligence people at the monthly target conference run by SOG and attended in Saigon by representatives of the major American commands in Vietnam. The USAF was appalled at the low payoff as they tried to retard the movement of enemy people and things to the south. All indications were that the enemy logistic effort was only marginally affected by attacks from the air. The Air Force wanted to find good targets, preferably targets not protected by dense jungle and enemy anti-aircraft weapons. Pilot eyeballs, sophisticated photography, infrared imagery, and the best space-age technology had proved inadequate in the search. It would be useful if a smelly recon guy stood on the trail while picking his nose and scratching his crotch, and then went for a walk to find out if there were parallel or intersecting trails. SOG took the mission and gave it to CCC. CCC gave it to Fat Albert. Key tracked it, A to Z.

Despite clear evidence of enemy use of neutral territory in Laos and Cambodia to support their forces in the south, the U.S. and North Vietnam played a game of "let's make believe." The North denied the existence of the trail. The United States claimed to respect the national sovereignty of Laos and Cambodia. Therefore, the U.S. couldn't use evidence of enemy violations of neutrality acquired while violating the neutrality of Laos and Cambodia, called Prairie Fire and Salem House respectively.

Hence the "sanitized" Recon Teams. There was no identification of either the American soldiers or their little mercenaries. Uniforms were non-standard. At first the RTs used non-U.S. weapons, with the Swedish K assault rifle and the Soviet AKs being the most common. Later in the war there were so many U.S. weapons—from World War II M-1 rifles to modern M-16s—used by both sides around the world that it hardly mattered. It soon became clear that the game inhibited both sides. A dead or captured American, evidence of the American game being played in the Prairie Fire and Salem House AOs, frustrated the bad guys who couldn't produce the American without explaining how they got him and what they were doing in the neutral countries bordering Vietnam. Men who weren't there were fighting other men who weren't there in a secret war within the one reported in the press. Both sides courted world opinion. Being caught red handed on the wrong side of the fence was bad form, but it happened from time to time.

***

After the emotional start, Bob Hahn settled down to a detailed and professional debriefing. Alabama was inserted without incident. Circling often on his own back trail to check for trackers, Fat Albert was satisfied that if there were any, they were standing off at such a distance that Alabama could go about its business. The RT headed for its initial point, always listening for trackers.

Perhaps the false insertions did the trick; perhaps they were just lucky; perhaps a tracker or two was following at a safe distance hours behind the RT out of fear of dirty tricks. In any event, the team moved without incident to an overnight position. From there they would head out on an azimuth of 270 degrees on the second day of the planned four-day mission.

Any RT had a fundamental decision to make about how it would travel. It could follow trails going in the right general direction. This option permitted speed. It also risked walking into an ambush. Alabama did not walk on trails, except to measure and photograph them. Then they were marked on the maps carried by the One-Zero and the One-One and noted in the mission logs maintained by both men.

The second option was to follow an azimuth and beat the bush, the safest way to move in an area thought to be secured by the enemy. But it was slow. Albert chose a third way to go, a combination of moving on game trails headed in the right general direction and following an azimuth where the jungle was not hopelessly thick. Baby-San was normally point man. Albert moved behind him.

Baby-San was the RT's best reader of signs in the jungle and an uncanny navigator. From time to time Albert would redirect him, but Baby-San was a man with a sixth sense. Some people have a magical something that defies rational explanation. They hear, see and sense things others—including the best-trained and most experienced soldiers—simply don't notice. Albert was satisfied to accept Baby-San's skills as a gift, like the ability to run fast. As he put it, Baby-San was born with a gyroscope and a compass up his ass. All he needed was for Fat Albert to point.

Two hours before dark, the RT moved on an azimuth as far as possible from all known trails. After an hour, the team stopped to eat cold, wet rice and to drink lots of water. There would be no cooking and little eating during the mission. Fire or smoke would almost certainly attract anyone in the vicinity. Recon men could never make clear to the uninitiated how adrenaline, fear, and concentration blotted out hunger.

After they ate and before they moved for the last time on day one, they erased all signs of human presence. Half an hour before total darkness, the team moved into dense vegetation with Albert leading. Baby-San brought up the rear rearranging the trail like a diligent gardener. The "remain overnight position," RON in military jargon, was nearby.

Albert stopped and nodded. Rucksacks were placed in a circle around him. This ballet had been choreographed by the One-Zero and rehearsed countless times in the Kontum training area. Without a word, each man opened his rucksack, removed a Claymore mine, and placed it, forming a perimeter some fifteen feet from Albert. When Baby-San returned to the perimeter after his gardening and was snugly inside, each man carefully adjusted his mine so that it dovetailed with the placement of the others to provide 360-degree coverage around the team, if detonated. Each mine was placed so that a tree or a fold in the ground was between the team and the mine. The mines were rigged for electrical detonation, and wires were fed out as each man returned to his rucksack. Albert had meanwhile pulled out a clacker, a detonator into which the mine wires were secured.

By pressing a button causing electrical contact to be made, bad things would happen to bad guys skulking too close to Fat Albert and his team. A God-awful explosion would strike such terror in a man that he would certainly feel ice cubes in his belly, and he would probably defecate. And that was the easy part. The hard part, at least for a millisecond, was having one's limbs torn off and body perforated by hundreds of small metal projectiles. Unlike earlier mines, much of whose blast was directed upward, Claymores sent their killer cones out parallel to the ground. Just as with a shotgun, the cone of projectiles was denser close to the source and sparser as the pellets spread out at a greater range. Since combat in the jungle was up close and personal, anyone in the path of a Claymore blast was either a dead man or so badly mutilated that he wished he were dead.

Fat Albert controlled the clacker. If the enemy threatened the survival of the team at night, he would detonate the mines at once to break contact in the general mayhem sure to follow. An additional positive feature was that unlike firing small arms, mines—like grenades—did not pinpoint the exact positions of the friendlies nor their number.

The first night passed quietly.

Stealth, slow movement, and strict attention to security characterized the activities of the second day. Albert searched for alternate trails to the known main trail before spending another uneventful night in a thicket some two kilometers still east of the main trail. Only small game trails were crossed. There was no sign of the enemy.

The third day would require all of Albert's cleverness, all of Baby-San's field craft, all of the training and discipline of Alabama, and one hell of a lot of luck. If the premise of the operation was validated, the enemy had patrols and outposts watching and listening for disturbers of their peaceful existence under the triple canopy not yet penetrated by American aircraft nor by foot patrols.

After a cold wet rice breakfast, Albert emphasized the need to stay off trails, to pause frequently, and to expect to hear rather than see NVA activity. They were barely out of the RON position when loud voices and gunfire—apparently the sounds of hunters celebrating a kill—suggested to Albert that the enemy troops were fat, dumb, and happy. It crossed his mind that he was listening to the kind of horseplay he enjoyed during rest periods in Nha Trang, and he was reminded that in this business, carelessness cometh before death.

The RT heard the sound of trucks. The Americans were immediately conscious of vehicles slowing, downshifting, and then powering up an incline. Both Albert and Hahn scribbled in their notebooks: "5 secs/ 8 veh/ 2-3 t." The trucks were moving at five-second intervals, and eight

Legacy of Lies

trucks were in that series. They sounded like two- to three-ton type trucks.

Albert wanted a peek at the road at several points so that he could pick a spot from which the team could monitor traffic. He also needed to find a place where the team would sooner or later cross the road to complete the recon of its far side. Using familiar hand signals, the plan unfolded. Albert and his point man would snoop at spots along the road; Hahn and three Yards would wait in place. Indicating his watch and shrugging, Albert let it be known that he couldn't tell how long the two would be gone, two hours, three, six? He would return to Hahn and the patrol base. If Albert and the point man were compromised, SOP in effect.

That required no explanation, for Alabama's Standard Operating Procedure was clear: When the One-Zero went forward for his leader's reconnaissance, Hahn called the shots for the rest of the team. If he thought Albert was dead or on the run, his guidance was to Charlie Mike, continue the mission.

Albert moved out. The rest of the team had been watching the dumb show. No one spoke. All gave a thumbs-up and settled into positions providing all-around security for the four men.

In the next several hours Hahn noted his watch and wrote in his pad each time he heard traffic, shouts, or gunshots. After four hours Albert and Baby-San returned grinning. "It's like an Autobahn. We got a good spot for an OP," Albert whispered to Hahn. He signaled, follow me.

The outpost permitted a view of a straight stretch of some thirty meters of road as it approached a curved hill. It was the widest and best surfaced portion of the clandestine supply route any of them had ever seen. From their vantage point they saw that the five-second interval represented about fifty meters between the trucks that traveled in packs of six to nine. In a period of about ten hours there were twelve packs, none with fewer than six trucks and none more than nine. Nine of the convoys went south with boxes stacked and secured in the cargo areas; three went north with litter patients and some wounded sitting on the benches.

39

That the cargo headed south and broken bodies headed north was not surprising, but the volume of truck traffic was. Even more impressive was the fact that bicycles and foot traffic shared the road with trucks. No one in Alabama had seen that before. Bicycle or foot traffic didn't usually move on roads suitable for trucks. The enemy didn't want a convergence of traffic to make a target of truck routes otherwise hidden from view. The NVA leadership assumed that the Americans weren't stupid. If all trails converged, they would drop bombs on suspected roads under the green concealment. The Americans seemed to have no shortage of bombs.

Albert motioned to Hahn, took him away from the road, and whispered:

"Compare notes."

He showed Hahn his notes and sketches and looked at Hahn's. Each consulted the other's notes and rounded out his. Then Albert fixed an intense pair of eyeballs on Hahn and hissed:

"Friend, this is the jackpot."

He paused.

"There's no bypass, no alternate. Get this all down. Shoot up all film on trail."

He paused again.

"Gotta cross the road and check. Almost certain we'll find no alternate trails, but gotta check."

Again he paused. Hahn had never seen Albert so keyed up.

"We confirm what's on the other side of this road. Then we get the poop back to Kontum."

Hahn nodded. He hadn't said a word. Albert had communicated with such passion that Hahn was afraid to speak.

Albert returned to the OP. Hahn followed.

***

Albert worried about roving patrols that might stumble upon the team if he stretched his luck for another day of watching from his current position. Two days of reporting traffic on the trail would cause much excitement in Saigon and at CCC, Albert mused, but if a patrol found him, the enemy would be alerted and the detailed information Alabama had gathered would be lost to higher headquarters. It was time to depart.

Since he had watched the curve on the hill almost all day and noted the absence of security forces, Albert decided to cross the road at that point just after dark. Every step of the RT was a step into the unknown; every precaution was an insurance policy; little things decided who lived and who died.

There were two ways to get the RT to the other side of the road. Albert could slip the team over one man at a time, or he could cross them in a line in one rush. He chose the latter, and they made it undetected. Some distance was put between the team and the road as Albert avoided the noise of thrashing about in terra incognita by directing Baby-San to take a heading through slightly sparser jungle. They were an estimated five hundred meters from the road when it happened.

Two trail watchers were preparing a meal when Baby-San came upon them. They were reaching for their weapons when Baby-San fired two short bursts from his CAR-15, killing both instantly at a range of ten meters. Only Albert saw what had happened. The others dropped to the ground immediately. Albert got them up and moved the team through the clearing as quickly as possible, noting the U.S. carbine and a rifle, probably a Mauser, near the two dead men. They wore mixed costumes of black pajamas and military uniforms. One was in a fetal position. The other died with his arms extended as though he were stretching.

Albert directed his point man into the thickest vegetation he could make out in the darkness. Under these light conditions the darker in color, the thicker the jungle. In thick undergrowth about a kilometer from the road, Albert set up the RON position. He was closer to the road than he wanted to be, but he didn't want to stumble into any more bad guys in an area that was obviously filled with patrols and listening posts. Twice during the night trucks could be heard downshifting to power up the hill.

At first light the Claymores were collected and the team had moved almost a kilometer when the trackers were heard. They had found the bodies and Alabama's trail. Albert sent Hahn and three Montagnards on the azimuth to extraction, while he and Baby-San delayed the trackers.

***

The narrative was finished. It was quiet. Ken Key paused before addressing Hahn.

"Bobby, I got an easy one and a tough one."

"Go ahead, Ken."

"First the easy one. From the time you crossed that main road, the Autobahn, you were pretty much on the run. I gotta confirm this. Did you cross any north-south trails between the big road and your extract point?"

"Negative."

"Not even a foot path?"

"Rog."

"Look at your map. There's the road, and there's where you came out. I make it two and a half klicks."

"Yeah. Straight line."

"Nothing north-south?"

"Nothing."

"The tough one. I'm gonna tell you what I got on Fat Albert. You correct me if I got it wrong."

"Go."

"The last time you saw him he carried Baby-San until he saw you waiting like he told you. Baby-San was WIA but took up rear security."

"Yeah."

"Albert signaled you to go. He held his weapon up and pointed in the direction he wanted you to go. You understood that you were to extract."

"Yeah."

"Bobby, anything further?"

"Anything from Covey on Albert?"

"Negative. Go get cleaned up and get some chow."

***

Hahn left the TOC with his first sergeant on one side and his company commander on the other. The CO joined Major Day and Major McCall, the supply officer. Radich realized that Mac had been waiting outside.

"You coulda joined us, Mac."

"Yes, sir. But it had started and I didn't want to break the flow. What's the word on Albert and the Yard?"

Radich spoke.

"Officially MIA. If they aren't dead I'd be surprised. Just in case, I want constant radio relay over the AO for the next week."

Day then provided some details of the debriefing for Mac, who swallowed often as he listened. Mac had been Albert's team commander when they had served previously in the II Corps Mike Force, the quick reaction force located in Pleiku. Mac noted that it was typical of Albert to remain with his point man and to cover the extraction of the main body.

"You two come with me," said the CO, leading them to his quarters where he poured about three fingers of good Irish whiskey into each of three glasses and raised his, saying:

"Fat Albert."

"To Albert."

"Albert."

They did that a few more times.

Janis, Kent State, CCC & 1970

In 1970 an earthquake in Peru killed 50,000 to 70,000 people; Janis Joplin died from a heroin overdose. Americans cared and knew more about the singer than about the Peruvians. She wailed "Me and Bobby McGee" almost constantly in the special operations camp near Kontum. The men liked the song a lot. Maybe it was "Freedom's just another word for nothing left to lose." Or, "I'd trade all my tomorrows for one single yesterday." Maybe Janis and the recon men were united in denial of the future, a frenetic grab at now. Maybe men join SF because they don't know about seminaries.

Ohio National Guard troops killed four students protesting the

Vietnam War at Kent State University. The Beatles released a hit, "Let It Be." Duly constituted authority gave draft-dodgers rifle bullets to kill war protesters on a college campus in America. Let it be. Americans invaded Cambodia then withdrew. Simon and Garfunkel released "Bridge Over Troubled Waters." The events were probably unrelated.

Rube Goldberg died in 1970. Shoulda been Secretary of State. So did Gypsy Rose Lee, John O'Hara, Erich Maria Remarque, and John Dos Passos. Alexander Solzhenitsyn didn't. He was awarded the Nobel Prize for Literature and lived in The Peoples' Republic of Vermont until he got homesick for Mother Russia and resumed his regular job there as Perpetual Pest.

Yukio Mishima committed public suicide in a Japanese way on a balcony in public. He plunged a knife in his belly. A friend whacked him in the neck with a big sharp sword. Chopped his head right off. That's what friends are for.

War films Patton, M*A*S*H*, Catch 22, and Little Big Man were released in 1970. Patton liked war. Most other folks didn't much care for it.

CCC men were good at war and living on the edge. The Studies and Observation Group assigned them not-quite suicidal missions. As the United States withdrew troops from Vietnam, the recon men chose to remain.

PJ Arrives in Vietnam

Paul John Riley landed at Saigon's Tan Son Nhut Airport for his first glimpse of Vietnam at about the time that Grady returned. He could have made the marathon trip first class, stretching his legs and sucking up martinis in a civilian luxury bird, but he flew with GIs in a government-leased aircraft. He wanted to record his initial impressions of men going to war. PJ had a severe case of the professional malady that comes from an overdose of energy, ambition and high intelligence: American-itis. He could not not work. He intended to place unassigned copy in the hands of his Saigon bureau chief at first sight. No one accused PJ of sloth.

Hot air entered, soldiers filed out, PJ slapped backs, shook hands, and wished his companions well, using current GI jargon. Winning the confidence of boony rats would be his ticket to professional success; nothing was more important to him.

"Watch your butt, man!"

"No John Wayne, dude!"

"Be cool."

Anxiety was behind the mask of bonhomie, showing confidence and intimacy, concealing fear. The prospect of death was on their minds as they were ushered from basic training to now, but cool was mandatory. They watched themselves playing parts in a film. The World War II formula played well. See the soldiers going to war; hear them confiding; see them parting. Brooklyn. Cracker. Manly. Unshaven. Noble. Naive. Add a black guy from central casting. Toss in a Latino.

At twenty-four, PJ was older than all but a few of his fellow travelers: regular NCOs returning for a second or third bite of the apple; pilots, closer to social security benefits than their first time in the voting booth; mature flight attendants choosing long layovers in Hawaii and a regular work schedule.

***

Soldiers were herded through the terminal. PJ followed signs to Passport Control. He showed ID to a Vietnamese in white uniform, a pistol on his hip and a clipboard in his hand. A local in black trousers and a white shirt spoke to the official, turned to PJ.

"Mr. Riley, welcome to Vietnam. I'm Cau from bureau. Please come with me."

He didn't miss a beat, walking and talking.

"Chief said take you to guesthouse. Have a drink. See TV. Crash and burn. When you get up, call number on night table after 10 a.m. I come get you. Then you talk to chief. Long trip makes people goofy. Best to sleep. This way to baggage."

PJ in tow, Cau glided through chaos. Bags rescued, they entered a white jeep parked close to the terminal with a windshield card proclaiming: PRESS. PJ was in heaven. He saw his recent fellow-passengers milling around a green bus with windows covered by wire mesh, their underarms dark with wet as they waited, scared and wondering what next?

Cau drove through smog. Beeping horns and screaming brakes punctuated the sounds of voices singing Vietnamese as they wove through the maze of pedestrians, bikes, cyclos, motor scooters, civilian cars, and military vehicles. Sidewalks were jammed with people and merchandise. American brands of cigarettes, alcoholic beverages and soaps shared the sidewalks with cripples, beggars and military clothing and equipment. Men wore white long-sleeved shirts open at the throat and black trousers, Cau's uniform. Beautiful women, delicate pastel flowers in Suzie Wong dresses, dotted the moving mass of humanity.

Turning, the white jeep left the busy world of crowds, noise, and garbage and entered another world, one of quiet streets lined with majestic trees. Behind the trees were walls. Behind the walls were placid villas. Sandbag bunkers and armed men were at the entrances to the villas, some discreetly tucked into foliage, others as bold as fortifications on the Maginot Line.

Cau stopped at the entrance to a particularly elegant residence. A guard with an automatic weapon at the ready blocked their way. He was accompanied by a uniformed partner with a mirror attached to the end of a long pole. The mirror was passed under the jeep. The man with the pole said something, and Cau drove into the compound.

"Cau, that wasn't Vietnamese."

"Good ear, Mr. Riley. That's Chinese. Security guys are from Cholon, the Chinese section of Saigon. Me too. Nungs are Chinese mercenary soldiers. Used to be from boondocks and good soldiers. Now Saigon cowboys. They look mean and hire for U.S. money."

"Call me PJ. Don't they trust you?"

"You mean security check? Routine. I'm happy. Maybe when I go for you at airport somebody sticks bomb under jeep. SOP."

"Can those guys shoot straight?"

Cau laughed.

"Some real good, some fakes. Like press and soldiers. Maybe like everybody."

PJ delighted in the confusion and press of the crowds downtown, the sight of delicate young ladies, and the security check. He was a little boy in a big candy store or on Santa's lap.

Cau opened the door to the guesthouse and waved PJ in. Tile floors, floor to ceiling windows, rattan chairs, teak tables, fragrant flowers, and slowly rotating ceiling fan created a feeling of cool and graceful repose.

"I think I'm going Asiatic," he mused, approving all he surveyed.

PJ smiled, noting that factotum Cau had gone Asiatic some years earlier.

A hasty tour revealed two bedrooms, a sitting room with desk and typewriter, kitchen, dining room, and full bath with a large tub and separate shower. A terrace provided a view of a flower garden, lush lawn, and tropical trees, all enclosed by a wall that surrounded the house and grounds. Sharp glass and barbed wire embedded in the top of the high walls and the presence of armed guards suggested that not all was well in paradise.

"Great digs," he thought as Cau gave him a key to the front door.

"I've died and gone to heaven."

Cau opened a liquor cabinet and pointed to a refrigerator.

"Best don't go out. Tomorrow we do briefing where is safe and where is danger. Food and beer in refrigerator. Call me after 10 a.m. when you feel rested. I go now."

"Join me for a drink?"

"Next time, PJ. I got business."

"Thanks for the introduction to Vietnam."

Cau left.

PJ barely suppressed a shout of glee. He had never felt so alive. He poured a gin and tonic, carried it to the desk, and sat. He put his fingers on the typewriter keys with great pleasure in a thought: war correspondent. It was delicious. But a voice said, this is a dangerous place.

PJ had a picture in his head. He would write about grunts the way Ernie Pyle reported about the dogfaces of WWII. Pyle told it right because he listened to combat soldiers. No big words. Tell the folks back home what you see, what soldiers say, and where they are from. And he had more recent models, near-contemporaries whose reputations had been made in the field and by challenging authority: David Halberstam, Peter Arnett, Neil Sheehan, Morley Safer, Stanley Karnow, Dan Rather. He would not settle for gossip, Army handouts, or happy talk from public affairs briefers. The story was men in combat. He would get the story. He wanted to join the first team. Ernie Pyle was first team.

Fred, Bureau Chief

A few hours with Fred on his first full day in country showed PJ that his boss was a pro, a mentor whose advice was intended to guide the rookie to success.

By 1970 there was a great divide between the old-timers of the press corps who prided themselves in hunt-and-peck typing and getting the story right and a new generation of ambitious graduates of top university journalism schools, some of whom failed to make a distinction between show biz and news biz. Some of the old school saw the younger ones as punk kids with credentials, a ticket to Saigon, and ego where a conscience was supposed to be. The new breed's willingness to step over bodies on the path to the top of the heap alienated senior craftsmen. Aware of Fred's blue-collar background, his state college degree, and his twenty-five year climb to the top of his craft, PJ respected Fred's generosity in tutoring a lad to the manor born. Later, as PJ observed how other older colleagues on the Vietnam beat treated their new guys, he would thank God for Fred.

While in New York, PJ had taken the trouble to learn something about his new boss. Fred graduated from a teachers college in 1941, joined the Army in January '42, fought in Africa, Sicily, and Italy, was wounded twice, and ended the war a captain with medals, one for valor. Fred remained in Europe after the war to cut his teeth with the Paris-based Herald-Tribune. He reported on the civil war in Greece, free elections that came close to putting Communists in power in France and Italy, and the 1948 Israeli-Arab War. Then, he signed on with the New York paper that claimed to print all the news fit to print. He covered the Berlin Airlift, the war in Korea, and the French war in Indochina until 1954. Assignments in Israel and Hong Kong followed before he returned to Saigon.

His wife, who called herself his souvenir from Vietnam One, was a lovely and cultivated Vietnamese lady, a Catholic from Hanoi. Their two girls in their early teens were as beautiful as their mother and as comfortable in Vietnamese and French as they were in English. Their Hebrew and Chinese, they confessed, were rudimentary.

Years later, PJ remembered that first day in Fred's company. Expecting brusqueness, indifference, vulgarity, or worse, he found graciousness. Fred was as interested in the young man's development as any of his teachers had ever been. After an hour, PJ almost called him Uncle Fred. They sipped coffee as the bureau chief reviewed PJ's vita aloud.

"Andover, history at Stanford, Fletcher School of Law and Diplomacy; six months with the paper in New York and off to Vietnam. Fast track. Your home of record is New York City. Military service, none. Hmmm. Osteomyelitis kept you out of the Army. Mickey Mantle shares your problem. Kept him out of Korea. But you'd have trouble with a major league curve ball. Unmarried. Did they get it right?"

"Everything but my fingerprints and blood type."

"We won't need your fingerprints, but it is in your interest to have your blood type on dog tags. And to wear the dog tags."

As he spoke Fred revealed that, sure enough, he had dog tags on the chain he wore around his neck.

"Take a look at this."

Fred passed a checklist to PJ.

"I'd want this kind of an orientation. My secretary will guide you through the paperwork: pay, ID, credentials, driver's license, press club membership, etc.

"Cau will take you shopping for suitable field and town clothing. He'll point out where you don't want to go and where you can go for food, drink, and social life. As a big city boy you'll appreciate what the fellow in The Music Man says, 'Ya gotta know the territory.'"

"At about 1600—by the way, begin telling time in the military manner. It's their bat, their ball, and their game. Besides, most of the world does it that way. At about 1600, Cau will deliver you here for the credentials you'll need for the MACV briefing at 1700. Attend, but don't worry about the substance. I have someone covering that. I want you to get the hang of things—meet the briefers, the Public Affairs Officers, some gentlemen of the press. See and be seen.

"Stop by the house at 1900 for a drink. I want to take you to dinner and to show you Saigon by night, and to talk.

"In the next two weeks, find your way around Saigon. Then some ops in the field, from IV Corps in the south to I Corps in the north. See 'em all: U.S. forces and allies; the good and the bad.

"Some loquacious colleagues will try to impress the new boy, but the biggest blowhards haven't had their butts off bar stools in Saigon in months. They get their material secondhand from real journalists who go to source to get it. We have the usual specimens from the human comedy in the Saigon press corps: saints and sinners, pros and fakes, intellectuals, drunks; and some drunken intellectuals.

"I'm not usually so preachy, but I want to get you off running. Any questions or comments?"

PJ, ever the good student, had been attentive, even fascinated.

"I'm too green to ask the right questions."

PJ hesitated before handing Fred his piece about the flight to Vietnam. Why not? It was good stuff.

"Here's copy we might want to use."

Fred didn't seem surprised. He scanned the text.

"Yes. I might be able to use this. We're doing a 'this week in Vietnam' feature. 'Vietnamization' is the buzzword for turning this mess over to our hosts. But GIs continue to arrive. Why send more troops here if it's over? Your copy may fit into that feature."

CHAPTER THREE

Concept: All Knuckleheads Are Equal

SOG Headquarters, Saigon

Colonel Pietro looked up from the summary account of Fat Albert's last mission. Staring through the wall of his Saigon office into the not-so-distant-past, he saw a demolitionist/linguist in his A Team in Germany in 1953—Fat Albert. "Best job I ever had," he mused, recalling a happy confluence of youth, travels in Europe, good men, skiing, Bavarian breakfasts, and a new German wife, when he was a captain. German bread, beer, and Gemütlichkeit, that untranslatable feeling of coziness, completed the picture in his mind's eye. There, in the 10th Special Forces Group in Bad Tölz, Albert hit his stride as a professional. A succession of assignments in Asia further honed his skills in combat.

Five years of honorable military service won American citizenship for the Lodge Act soldiers selected from the "displaced persons" destitute in Europe after the Second World War. Citizens born in the Promised Land took its blessings for granted; those who earned citizenship through service valued that prize, more with each passing year.

51

The Lodge Act, he reflected, was, like the CARE packages and the Marshall Plan after World War II, generous. But generosity profited the United States. Give and receive in ten-fold. It was the right thing to do for men who had nothing but the clothes on their backs when they came to us, and it gave us soldiers who would serve into the 1980s—if they could stay alive. They were the backbone of Special Forces, our foreign legion. They remembered when they had nothing, and strangers embraced them, at first gingerly, then without reservation. Grateful for what they later enjoyed as Americans, they brought empathy to their relations with the Vietnamese, the losers of the '50s and the '60s just as the Lodge Act men had been the losers of the '40s.

The old colonel was happiest in the company of real soldiers, listening to their BS, noting their pride and confidence, feeling himself one with them. He loved the cocky bastards prepared to let it all hang out, and he was their big daddy. Albert wasn't the first son he lost. Nor would he be the last.

Pietro spoke in a conversational tone:

"Sergeant Conway."

"Yessir," responded the senior sergeant from the doorway. He had anticipated the call since placing the message in the middle of the colonel's desk, not in the "IN" box. This was not routine bumpf. Since he screened most of the papers that crossed Pietro's desk, Conway had read it. He knew his boss. The TWX would rock the SOG boat.

"Jerry, ask Captain Hilfe and Captain Black to stop by at their earliest convenience."

"Yessir."

Conway had already alerted Hilfe, the Prairie Fire desk officer who knew more about Laos than anyone in the headquarters. Summoning Black, the Salem House desk officer, meant that the boss chose to broaden the discussion to include Cambodia. Conway interpreted the courteous colonel's, "at their earliest convenience," precisely as intended: "Get them in here, now!"

Pietro waited for the officers he affectionately called "my smartasses" as he reviewed the bidding. Interest in SOG's work at high levels had advantages. Quality resources, people and things, were promptly provided. But the price for high priority was the tendency of staff officers in Washington and Hawaii, kindred souls, to know too much about his business and to meddle in his field operations. Simply stated, "Those bastards will jump in my shit." He had to move quickly.

He admitted that he had behaved the same way when he was JSOA, the colonel with staff responsibility for Joint Special Operations Activities, in Washington. It was irresistible. An old special ops guy just had to get into the nitty-gritty. Monitoring SOG activities from his perch in the Pentagon, the JSOA put him right on top of the most interesting stuff going on in Vietnam. Hell, outside of Latin America, it was the only red-hot stuff going on in the whole defense establishment, Pietro's universe. NATO-Warsaw Pact confrontation, now in its third decade, was a constant, rather like the weather with good and less good days.

Access to top political-military decision makers is power. Pietro had been the junior military man routinely present in Washington discussions of special operations, but the generals, admirals, and politicos deferred to him for his expertise. They wanted to avoid looking foolish in front of the other big guys. His lifetime of bold and unorthodox activities produced original thinking that attracted the attention of political authorities tired of the pedestrian types whose thinking was conditioned by careers spent doing the ordinary very well.

That was heady stuff. His recommendations found their way to policy pronouncements. His exact words sometimes appeared in the Washington Post, credited to one of his bosses. Once, in a press conference, the President uttered Pietro's words. That pleased him, he confessed. Why not? He met with men who regularly met with the Secretary of Defense and the President of the United States. He had no respect for the SECDEF, who was set on a course without regard to military advice or inconvenient facts of any kind, but he had briefed him. Not bad for a kid whose introduction to unconventional war began as he dangled from a parachute over Japanese occupied Indo-China in 1945. Sometimes he thought that those months as a corporal in the boondocks were the best of his life. God, that was exciting. Adults get that stuff out of their systems. He never did. Nor did the men whose respect meant so much to him.

Now he was Op 35, commander of SOG's ground component. Jack Plunkett, former Op 35, was in Pietro's old slot at the elbow of the Chairman, JCS. He and Jack had flip-flopped assignments six months earlier. Jack would not be able to avoid second-guessing at the operational level any more than Pietro had when he was in Washington. The incestuous world of special ops insured that "the old guys" filled most of the command and senior staff positions from the boonies up the chain to DC. That expedited the coordination of operations, but few of the old warhorses could resist jumping into the middle of the action at the tactical and operational levels. Maybe that was why none of them were in danger of promotion to general officer. The point? Pietro didn't need meddling from Jack—or from Mark.

***

Mark Burns—old dog, new colonel, special ops senior staffer in Honolulu—believed he had a monopoly on truth, beauty, justice, and the American Way. His philosophy was: "Don't just stand there! Kill something!" He was another friend in court, but his superheated energy made him a pain in the ass. On the other hand, he had the ear of the admiral who was CINCPAC, Commander-in-Chief, Pacific Command.

Jack Plunkett was a different case, circumspect and infinitely brighter than Burns. Insiders in the Washington pol-mil game correctly identified him as an excellent soldier and a skilled political player, a good choice for the job he was doing. Chance played its part. The difference between who lived and who died, who became a general, who was booted out after a war, who sat in a key job or a bullshit job, all of this was a matter of inches or seconds. Jack had become the indispensable colonel who would never be a general.

Army folk wisdom had it that one Special Forces assignment was OK. That showed that a guy had a pair of balls. More than one such assignment showed that he had shit for brains. The careerists regarded SF as a sideshow. Or they punched that ticket once, just in case there was a pay-off somewhere down the line. After all, Jack Kennedy had given them their green berets. So, the officers who focused on stars volunteered for SF along with the guys who had shit for brains. But Kennedy was killed, and the orthodox continued to run the paper-shuffling army, the real army most of the time. The old sweats stuck it out in SF for the pure joy of Service with good men doing essential work. The star seekers returned to "the real army" for the most understandable of reasons: to get ahead. Some of those who had done one gig with SF, plus conventional types, listened to the old SF guys and even sought their advice. And the Air Force and Navy had jumped on the special ops bandwagon. The true believers had something good going. Wars separate the clerks and jerks from the warriors, and many of the former were on staffs at all levels. When God made a lot of poor folks, he also made a lot of clerks and jerks.

Pietro snapped from his reflection to the here and now.

He wanted to keep the good guys informed. They could help, but he didn't want anyone kibitzing in his mission or jabbing their chopsticks in his rice bowl.

"If Jack, Mark, and I are on the same sheet of music, we can do the country some good," Pietro thought. "If I can start it up the chain, and Mark can get the admiral to bless my plan, Jack can run it through the Puzzle Palace like nobody else."

He turned back to the summary of Alabama's debriefing sitting in the middle of his desk. It had been sent simultaneously from Kontum to Saigon, Honolulu and Washington. This was not standard military routing. Normally reports move up the chain link by link, the same way orders came down, but higher headquarters carefully monitored the politically sensitive cross-border ops. Knowledge is power, especially in bureaucracies. Since the most interesting aspect of the war in Vietnam—which was simultaneously winding down and being lost—was the clandestine cross-border show, the bosses in Hawaii and Washington were very attentive to it. So the staffs cared. SOG got lots of attention and lots of advice, some from has-beens, and some from the never-wuzzes. Presidential interest got everybody interested. Given the political climate of 1970, the American public and the media, mused Pietro, would become very interested if we were to catch a tit in the wringer—like exposure of our routine violation of Cambodian and Laotian neutrality.

Yes, Alabama's debrief would get the attention of military insiders. There weren't many on the SOG distribution list. Those who were would note immediately that an RT got a look at a chunk of terrain previously not seen by an American. "If I don't make a sound recommendation, quickly," he thought, "the bright boys in PACOM and JCS will be happy to help, quickly."

Pietro's Smartasses

Conway burst into the colonel's ruminations.

"Sir, the Prairie Fire and Salem House desk officers are here."

"Bring 'em in. And join us."

The brain trust, two captains and a master sergeant, assembled at a conference table that formed a T with Pietro's desk and took seats in no particular order, except that the colonel remained at his desk at the top of the T. In Pietro's outfits the sergeants were expected to engage in such war councils and to follow their natural inclination to call unmitigated bullshit unmitigated bullshit. The colonel put it quaintly: In this outfit, all knuckleheads are equal.

"Help yourselves." He waved at the bottomless pitcher-shaped coffee thermos, which sat fueled on the table as long as anyone from Ops 35 was in the headquarters building on Rue Pasteur.

"You saw the Alabama report. What do I recommend to my boss and his bosses?"

Since the colonel was looking at him, Rick Hilfe, the Prairie Fire expert, began:

"Sir, I did some checking. Average stay time for a team in that area over the past two years is measured in minutes. We extracted teams within an hour, because the enemy was on 'em on the LZ. There were also hot LZs denying infiltration. In a couple of cases both the primary and alternates were hot. When we got teams on the ground they ran into contacts real fast. We've lost six KIA and had fifteen WIA in eight contacts in there over the last two years."

"OK, Rick. Go on."

"I also checked my holdings against Air Force intel, sir. It confirms Alabama's findings: There's only one north-south trail in the area."

"No alternate or parallel trails?"

"We can't see through the triple canopy, but neither photos, heat sensors, nor seismic monitors suggest an alternate trail. Air Force recce birds have checked day and night. Army Mohawks with side-looking radars can't find anything. Current intel confirms history. Looks like one trail there. Just one. Unless we have a better idea, I think the Air Force will frag beaucoup Arc Light missions on the trail."

Arc Lights were the B-52 bomber strikes from altitudes so high that the poor bastards on the ground couldn't see or hear the aircraft. There was no escape from direct hits, but often—usually, if the truth were known—the missions just knocked down a lot of trees. Russian trawlers off Guam, home base to most of the B-52s flying the missions in Vietnam, provided early warning to their allies. The enemy didn't know where the bombs would fall, but he did know when they would fall. The trawlers reported takeoff; simple speed and distance computations allowed Hanoi to pass a general alert for a certain time frame of danger to all of its forces with which it had communications. Enemy commanders ordered their troops into deep holes in the ground for a couple of hours to minimize casualties. It was literally hit or miss.

"Salem House, anything to add?"

"I don't think there's another choke point like that anywhere on the trail in Cambodia. The terrain in the south allows alternate land routes, and rivers are used to transport in sampans or to float stuff downstream. It's different in the Laotian mountains. Albert certainly found something important. Too bad we don't know exactly how long that stretch of trail is without alternates. In brief, we never found anything like this before."

"Thanks."

Pietro turned to the sergeant.

"Jerry?"

"Sir, don't let the Air Force make splinters of the woods. Even if they hit the son of a bitch, the bad guys will patch it up. I don't think much of using that high tech stuff to knock down low-tech trees.

Making holes in the road ain't the way to go. They'll just fill 'em in."

"OK. Jerry takes us right to the point. What do I tell my boss to tell Washington? Rick."

The reflective Hilfe had been studying Prairie Fire for two years, the last eighteen months from Saigon and before that from Da Nang. Watching Laos was his hobby and his job. He looked more the professor or accountant than John Wayne.

"I want to know how long that road runs without an alternate."

Jerry Conway, usually respectful when disagreeing with the officers in the headquarters, exploded, spraying a little spittle along with the words:

"Bull shit! More recon, more guys hurt! We got a terrific target. Exploit it! Foreplay is over. Let's get with it! Those dipshits in Hawaii and Washington will get their dicks caught in a zipper. Go for it! We should exploit soonest!"

Hilfe never batted an eye.

Black chimed in:

"I agree with Jerry. Draw a goose egg around that place where Alabama observed the road and you come up with a good target. We have a choke point. We have a target. Let's react."

Rick Hilfe took none of this personally, but he would never be satisfied with the approximate when the precise was almost within reach. Jerry Conway was predisposed to direct action. His solution to most problems was to go for the throat, the eyes, and the groin, without calculating how many angels could fit on the head of a pin. He'd snuff the angels with white phosphorous.

Pietro allowed the discussion to run its course before returning to the issue he faced.

"OK. It boils down to get more intel or exploit. Given what we know and a blank sheet, how would you put maximum hurt on the enemy?"

Reflective Rick responded first. It was an interesting problem, the kind that Rick liked to solve.

"Sir, I have a concept, but the details need to be worked out by the killers."

"Go."

"Start with the basic template of ends, ways, and means. The end is to interrupt the enemy flow of people and things to the south so that our allies can get on their feet before the U.S. forces leave Vietnam. The way is to trap as many vehicles on that stretch of road with no escape and then to destroy them and kill the people. The killers should decide the means, but it has to be more than we ever put over the fence before. I mean troops on the ground."

"Tell me what you have in mind?"

"Two options."

Rick had their attention.

"One, a force somewhere between a battalion and a brigade of light infantry, maybe the Cav or the 101. They require a lot of air assets and ground combat power. But that flunks the political test of plausible denial.

"Two, SOG does it with minimal force and plausible denial with one to two hundred friendlies on the ground, mostly indig troops. Beef up an exploitation company and several RTs. Max air. We block and stop the enemy on that choke point. Then our air blows 'em away. This buys time for ARVN to do what Washington wants: Vietnamization."

Black liked what he heard.

"All SOG and air assets could be dedicated to this mission if we suspend all other ops. I like using reinforced RTs to seal off the kill zone. Conventional forces are a non-starter."

Conway caught the fever.

"Rog! Gotta be SOG assets. If the politicians buy off on it, we can make it happen. We back up enemy logistics for miles and miles and give the Air Force an Olympic class orgasm. Give 'em observed targets for a change."

The colonel's Washington experience told him that what was crazy talk one day could be policy the next, if the pols needed something bad enough. Vietnamization just might allow SOG to do its thing. ARVN needed time to get its act together if it were to hang tough after the Americans were gone. The American people were tired of the war. Give it back to the Vietnamese, ready or not, was the attitude.

Interrupting enemy logistics would be a leg up for Saigon. The concept made good sense for a bunch of reasons. Pietro's colleagues in Hawaii and Washington would have a better feel for the political climate in high places.

Two junior officers and a sergeant had filled his head with sugarplums. Staff discussions in Washington would have been characterized by a lot of hedging and equivocation. The ribbon clerks would "on the other hand" until you were dealing with an octopus. His smart-asses cut through all that stuff. They got to essentials. He wondered if they would one day degenerate into senior toadies in a peacetime army. Good guys could be emasculated by service on what the Army called "high-level" staffs. Periods of peace lead to an army of all show no go. We need two armies, one for parades and one to fight.

"Thanks, troops. Jerry, I want to talk to Burns and to Plunkett as soon as they get to work. Keep this under your hats. You know how fast news of a hot mission travels in this outfit."

"Almost like a prairie fire," quipped the Prairie Fire captain.

"Out!" said the boss.

CHAPTER FOUR

The Players: Old Heads & Rookie Journalist

Mark

Mark Burns was a contentious figure in the Special Forces fraternity, partially because he was misunderstood and partially because he was understood. NCOs who had worked closely with him believed he got so wrapped up in the mission that he didn't give a rat's ass for the welfare of his troops. He killed a gaggle of enemy troops, but he also got a lot of good guys dead or badly hurt. Survivors and insiders accused him of being a glory hound who craved recognition, a man perfectly capable of striving for advancement or honors over the dead bodies of his soldiers. He also inclined to volcanic rages during which he would say outrageous things, followed by periods of contrition during which he apologized to his victims. The troops called him Dr. Death.

But others called him a brave son of a bitch. He accepted the most dangerous missions without hesitation or reflection. His supporters emphasized that he didn't send men to their deaths and injuries; he was with them when they got their lumps. He got his lumps as well, including a metal plate in his head, a gut shot wound, and a couple of exotic tropical diseases that come with the turf in Asia. How the head wound affected his thought process stimulated a game that could be played in a club or in someone's hooch while the booze flowed and war stories were spun. It was generally agreed that plumbing his psyche would keep a platoon of shrinks busy for a lifetime.

Some questioned his judgment; others went so far as to call him just plain dumb. Even before he was shot in the head it was said of him that he was a good guy on the ground; you just wouldn't want him to plan an operation, at least not one that you would go on. He was loud and garrulous. He was a former football player at a university more distinguished for alumni in the National Football League than in Phi Beta Kappa chapters. It was alleged that few grads of his school could read without lip movement. In brief, even those prepared to credit him with physical courage regarded him as the quintessential redneck. But he had a saving grace: He wanted to die in battle and earn the Medal of Honor.

How the warrior became a staff officer high in the chain of command reflects the way the U.S. military goes about its business.

Show and Tell

Some months before the Alabama mission, the admiral who was CINCPAC was in Saigon for an update on the course of the war when Mark Burns came to his notice. The admiral was singularly unenthusiastic at the prospect of yet another optimistic briefing as the war turned to shit. He regarded the formal MACV briefings much as the journalists regarded their "five o'clock follies," the daily press conference at which the media and the military waged their own war. Journalists had lost confidence in the military briefs and public affairs officers. So had CINCPAC. He told his staff in private that the Army briefings were "as illuminating as a fancy flashlight without a battery." He endured them to avoid the charge that the Navy had gone over to the enemy. Burns' remarks at the briefings struck the admiral as the only burst of honesty he heard in a full day of handsome colored charts, military jargon, and a level of analysis suitable for day-care centers. Mark's presence was an accident. Maybe it was an act of God.

Recovering from some exotic malady, Mark was working as a special assistant to the SOG commander when the CINCPAC arrived in Saigon for a round of briefings. His boss sent him to brief current SOG operations with a simple admonition:

"Mark, brief from the notes my staff has prepared. Answer the admiral's questions. Get back here without getting me in trouble. Do you have any problem with these instructions?"

"No, sir."

What followed wasn't entirely Mark's fault, but the SOG commander never did make general.

Those in the know said they never saw the Army four-star more pissed than he was on the day Mark briefed the grumpy old salt. Uncharacteristically, the Army four-star, often called an eagle scout, blistered the paint off the walls of his headquarters with language that never before or since crossed his lips.

The show was going as planned until Mark's brief turn on stage pleased the admiral and enraged the general. Spiffy briefers, slim and lithe in their starched jungle fatigues and spit-shined jungle boots, spoke in mellifluous tones. Headquarters warriors, unencumbered by personal experience in the mysteries revealed, succeeded one another in a ballet as flawless as the Bolshoi, though lacking a single spectacular leap. Until Mark's solo act.

The drone of the air conditioning accompanied the drone of the talking heads. Charts, photos, graphs, and text came together in a masterful explanation of the riddles of the known world. This headquarters had more answers than questions. The future of the Republic was in good hands.

Mark's teeth weren't perfect, his voice wasn't tuned to the air conditioner, and his boots had the look of having been walked in. Worse. He seemed to know and care about his subject. He stuck to the SOG script. Then, alas, the admiral interrupted his recital.

"Colonel, how did those guys tap the cable?"

"Sir, they used a spring loaded clamp with sharp..."

"Goddamn it, I don't mean that! How did they get there? If there's a fat cable, there's a big headquarters with lots of security."

"Infiltration was by parachute into triple canopy at night..."

"How the hell did they do that?"

Burns didn't know why the admiral beat him up for presenting an objective report, but he didn't like it. The admiral and Burns had bad tempers and rich vocabularies. Mark was close to big trouble, not for the first time in his career.

"Admiral, they jumped in fucking smoke-jumper gear, padded suits and masks, kinda' like fencing masks. Two of the four men were injured on infiltration, but they continued the mission..."

"Stop! They jump. They're a hundred or a hundred and fifty feet in the top of a tree at night, in a denied area. What happens next?"

"They git outta the fuckin' trees! They use drop lines to get down, reassemble, and continue the mission."

"Have you had people seriously hurt using this method?"

"Affirmative. We've had people killed doing it."

"Isn't there a better way?"

"We're trying every goddamned way we know how. What did you have in mind?"

The admiral's executive officer, an experienced commander of ships at sea, a four-striper, a long-time observer of the admiral, and a witness to four earthquakes and one volcano eruption, visibly cringed. No one addressed his boss in such an antagonistic manner. The President of the United States of America treated this sea dog in a deferential manner. Shit! An almost human being was about to be eaten. The admiral did not bite; he just nibbled. The XO was stunned at the admiral's calm rejoinder:

"I'll ask the questions. You answer. Tell me how you put people into Laos and Cambodia."

Burns warmed to the sailor's interest in the nuts and bolts of combat operations in a denied area characterized by inhospitable terrain and uncongenial people.

"Sir, most LZs and DZs in Laos are secured or observed by the enemy. Using chopper insertions was the way we did it for years. We got away with that in 1964. About 1968-1969, the enemy got smart.

Now half the chopper inserts are aborted or we gotta take teams out under pressure real fast. We use free fall from 10,000 feet with some success. But that's a big problem for reassembly on the ground. Even if the team maintains visual contact using infrared goggles, contact is lost in the last seconds as jumpers prepare for landing. Then they gotta link up in a denied area in the dark. That can take hours and it's hairy. There's a bunch of skills involved. This is a limited use technique. There ain't no grass lawns out there. If you don't land in forest, it's tall sharp grass. Assembly at night in Indian country with a major pucker factor is a bitch. Looking for one another is tricky. You can't be sure if you should blow a guy away or shake his hand."

"I see that. Tell me about other ways."

"Commando Vault, a 10,000 pound bomb with a long rod on the nose, is a way to blast a hole in the jungle big enough for a chopper to land or hover, so troops can jump out. Problem is if you are slow getting there, the bad guys are already there, waiting to shoot you. You can't hide a big bomb blast, so it's a foot race with the bad guys. If you arrive too soon after the blast, the jungle is still falling down. The big trees endanger troops and choppers. Visibility is shitty. There's so much dust and debris in the air right after the detonation that we have to wear gas masks that further limit what you can see, what with sweat and dust."

CINCPAC, attentive to Mark's remarks, commented: "You could walk teams in, but they need to go so far on foot that you would have to tip off their presence by resupplying them."

He was clearly interested in the techniques used and how the game was played.

"That's right, sir. We do walk people in. We do that in a couple of programs we run. But then you gotta trust the agent, 'cause you can't use Americans. Physical characteristics and language rule them out as guys just walkin' down the road in the middle of Laos or Cambodia. We use local types for that. When we run agents it's hard to know what they saw and what they made up to keep drawing pay."

"OK. It's difficult to get people in there, especially people with white faces. But you mentioned capturing a truck driver in Laos. How was that done?"

"Admiral, pure guts. Our team was tracked from insertion. Using mines, sniping, and ambushes, the RT commander covered his own ass while making it to the objective area to snatch the guy."

"How?"

"Sir, one of our tigers, a captain, plunged into the objective area, put his team on the side of a road, shot up three trucks, and grabbed the NVA soldier driving the second truck. They put a sandbag over his head, a rope around his neck, and hauled ass to an LZ and a chopper that took him to Kontum."

The admiral found the colonel's responses refreshing and wondered why his bluff frankness was the exception rather than the rule in a profession that took pride in directness and integrity.

"I want to shift gears. Did you hear the briefer before you describe the search and destroy missions for the next ninety days?"

"Yes, sir."

"Did you hear how a battalion was planned for a specific area two and three months from now?"

"Yes, sir."

"Give me your professional opinion of that."

Two thoughts raced through Mark's mind before he engaged his jaws. His boss at SOG wanted to keep his tits out of the wringer, and he wanted the admiral's questions answered. Hell, one out of two ain't bad.

"Admiral, that's just plain dumb!"

"Presumably you have a basis for your opinion."

"Yessir. In the first place, who knows what's gonna be in an AO two and three months from now? We got it backwards. The operations guy tells the intel guy, 'we're going in there. Tell me what's there.' It should be the other way around with the intel guy telling the ops guy that he has a good target.

"In the second place, why have a big bunch of people stomping around when a small team of good soldiers could snoop and find the bad guys? Small teams find 'em. Then pile on and knock the shit out of them. Small teams find 'em. Rifle companies fix 'em, kill 'em, and bring in arty and air power on observed targets. That's the way I'd do the job."

The admiral knew that the colonel was not speaking from a script. He was thinking on his feet and answering as honestly as possible. And he wasn't winning points with the Army four-star who, at the moment looked like he was sucking a lemon. The admiral realized that he had led Burns down the garden path. Burns went on as though he either didn't know he was on thin ice, or just didn't give a damn. He was not earning high marks for "tact," an entry on the Army's Officer Efficiency Report, his report card.

"It's dumb having big U.S. units beatin' the bush. Every day we get good kids hurt for nothin.' They trip mines, get hit by a sniper who shoots and is gone, and they fall over from heat exhaustion from carryin' too much useless shit around. Instead of resting in the shade full of piss and vinegar, ready to kick ass when recon finds the enemy, our guys are shootin' their wad stumble-dickin' around the bush. We got numbers that show it. A rifle company goes out for four days with a constant flow of air traffic bringing ice cream and other bullshit to them that tells the bad guys where they are. The enemy hides and jumps up when they want to give the Americans some grief. The U.S. unit never even sees the enemy. Then we brag that they never whipped us in the field. Shit, we're like the redcoats. We sure don't behave like an army that cut its teeth Indian fighting."

"And what are the consequences?"

"Sir, the enemy kicks our ass every day. We don't see them, and we lose people on every dumb ass company search and destroy operation. They're wearin' us down. College kids ten thousand miles away in the States see that. Them war protesters see it. The rifleman sees it. The point man has to wonder what all those officers and rear area mothers are thinkin' about. He's got it figured: The lifers must be the only dummies who don't see it."

The admiral nodded his head. He had provoked the briefer into a scathing critique of the unimaginative operational concepts of his host, who looked at the moment as if he had switched from lemons to vinegar. Much of what he had just heard was new information to the

CINCPAC. The U.S. military in Vietnam had compounded bad policy and strategy decisions in Washington with bad operational decisions in Saigon and bad tactical decisions at all levels. He needed someone who knew the score if his headquarters was to track Vietnamization and the course of the ongoing American pullout.

"How long have you been in-country?"

"Two and a half years on this tour and five out of the last six years, sir."

"All in special ops?"

"Yessir."

"What will happen in this country when we pull out?"

Burns didn't hesitate:

"It will look like Hanoi whipped us, no matter how we sugar up that pill. If Giap and Ho can tell their people that they whipped France and the U.S., they can convince their people to hang tough for final victory against Saigon. ARVN will screw around for a year or two. Then the bad guys will win."

"Do you have any specific ideas about how we can give ARVN what it needs to survive?"

"Sir, I'd like to think that through rather than just popping off about something so important to us and them. We are now at a level above my pay grade, but if the U.S. couldn't defeat Hanoi, Saigon sure as shit won't. As we go out the front door, I figure Uncle Ho will come in the back door. Anything to slow down the bad guys helps. That won't win the war, but it could give ARVN time."

"Colonel, thank you."

Personnel Manglement in Action

What followed was also above Burns' pay grade. The admiral told his executive officer to get Burns assigned to CINCPAC's staff as his special operations staff officer. The XO chose to "work the problem" in DC rather than in Saigon. Despite the folk wisdom that presumes a degree of acrimony between the Army and the Navy that prohibits cooperation, a few phone calls resulted in orders to Burns from the Army's personnel management. The Navy captain knew a guy who knew a guy.

The XO was one of some twenty maritime officers—sailors and marines—who attended the U.S. Army War College each year. One of his Army seminar mates from that happy experience was a flesh peddler for the Army. The captain called the colonel; the colonel went to his boss, a two-star High Potentate of People, and said:

"CINCPAC wants..."

"Whatever Lola wants, Lola gets."

"...a SOG lieutenant colonel, by name, promotable, to be his special ops guru."

"Give me one reason why I should say no to our admiral in the Pacific, who—it is rumored—is well wired to the White House."

"I can't think of nary a one, general."

"Anything else I need to know about it?"

"Purely info, sir. It's soon-to-be Colonel Mark Burns; long time SF; six years in RVN; now with MACVSOG; often shot; about time he renewed his acquaintanceship with mama in Hawaii. I think I owe the SOG commander a call. Just to keep him informed."

"Yep, we don't need any pissed off commanders. If he has heartburn, take my name in vain."

"Roger, sir."

"Do it. Thanks."

Chief SOG, the forever colonel, had no heartburn upon learning that good ole Mark would defend freedom from Hawaii. Burns was an accident waiting to happen. The Army four-star got apoplectic whenever he heard Mark's name, so his staff shed no tears as they bid aloha to him. Mark thus became the admiral's problem.

Burns was upset. A Medal of Honor is not won in Hawaii—at least not since 7 December 1941. And the war in Vietnam was winding down. It might be tough to get back before it was over, but he knew the score. Army leadership in country rejoiced at his departure. The SOG commander, extricating his tits from the wringer, was prepared to manage without him; so was the Army four-star whose search and destroy operational concept had been trashed by the loudmouth colonel. Burns consoled himself with the thought that he was still in special ops and would make frequent staff visits to Vietnam.

Washington

John Plunkett, Joint Special Operations Activities (JSOA), Joint Chiefs of Staff, the Pentagon, was the antithesis of Burns. Men either loved or hated Burns, and the latter were in the majority. Jack, no less firm in his views, seemed to have no enemies.

He was a preppie graduate of Groton, a graduate of the United States Military Academy, a Rhodes scholar, and a member in good standing of the much maligned eastern establishment that ran the nation before Texas poor boys and a Californian who wore dress shoes on the beach moved into the White House.

Unlike his Groton classmates, who sought the shortest routes to commissions in the Navy or to flight programs—if they served in the military at all—Jack wanted to be an infantry soldier and the Alvin York of the Second World War. He served in the 82nd Airborne Division as an enlisted soldier in World War II, made three combat jumps, got shot once, and was awarded a Silver Star and a Bronze Star. Discharged almost immediately after the war in the Pacific ended, he returned to the United States intending to follow the family tradition at Harvard. He had had a nice war and was a platoon sergeant when he left the Army. Neither he nor those who knew him even considered a military career for the heir of the patrician New England family.

Years later when asked why he rejoined the Army, he said that he missed being around real people doing real things. The camaraderie in a rifle squad was the most memorable experience in his life. Late in his freshman year at Harvard he informed his father that he had an appointment to West Point and intended to report there in the coming summer. His father sat him down, poured two whiskies, and made a short speech.

"What you have decided to do is one of the most foolish things I've ever heard. Should your sanity be restored in the coming year or two, I suggest that you return to Harvard. I'm quite sure that could be arranged. Meanwhile, to your health!"

They drank.

The older man believed banking or law were more suitable activities for his son, but he also knew that the young man would make his own decision. The subject was never raised again, and Jack never regretted his decision. During hazing at West Point, he reminded himself that most fraternities have initiations, and most young men are mindless.

Ranger School followed the Basic Infantry Officer Course at Fort Benning, and then it was off to England. From the clouds of Oxford he proceeded to the mud of Korea late in that war. He was wounded in a foot while a rifle platoon leader in a Ranger Company, mended in Japan, and insisted upon returning to his company despite a foot that bled on long marches for the rest of his career. He was a charter member of Special Forces at Fort Bragg and was in the first contingent sent to Germany. Except for the usual professional schools and battalion command in the 82nd Division, he spent his career in special operations. It was in the 10th Special Forces Group in Bad Tölz, Germany, where he met the men whose lives would intersect with his for the rest of his days in uniform. Both his CO and the youngest trooper in the 10th would agree, using their own words, that the captain was the quintessential professional: He had his shit together.

He was considered a someday Chief of Staff, but those wiser in the ways of the world knew that his choice to join the SF "sideshow" almost certainly meant that the highest grade he could expect was colonel. Generals were chosen from what was called the mainstream. His academy classmates encouraged him to return to the mainstream, but they recognized that special ops were to him a kind of calling. He was far more interested in the work itself than in advancement in rank, though he fully realized that high rank was useful in getting the right things done. In a sense he had the best of it by doing it his way. He remained close to the soldiers he loved—the independent rogues who were the backbone of SF—and his personal reputation as both combat soldier and military intellectual provided him with clout out of proportion to his rank. He had the ear of the Army's movers and shakers and the respect and affection of the rank and file. A professional soldier could want no more.

The old boy net, nepotism, influence peddling, insiders, and "the establishment" are words that conjure up pejorative reactions in the minds of most Americans raised in an egalitarian tradition. However, the same egalitarians, responsible for tough and important tasks, would surely prefer working with trusted and competent colleagues to working with strangers. So it is at the top of the military heap. Several of Jack's classmates had stars. They were scattered around the Army, some landing in Washington during Jack's watch there. He enjoyed cordial relations with most of his colleagues. He saw them on the job, over cups of coffee in the Pentagon, over drinks at the clubs around town, and at Founder's Day annually celebrating the establishment of the Military Academy. Interestingly, the old boy with the most clout was a close friend from their West Point days who was also not a front runner for stars: Karl Berenson.

Karl was the smartest man Jack knew. He was a colonel on the National Security Council staff and, allegedly, a confidant and protégé of the President's National Security Advisor. As a matter of fact, "Himself" leaned heavily on Karl for all sorts of things in addition to military expertise. The President's NSC Advisor recognized Karl as a legitimate phenomenon. Cats land on their feet, birds fly, and Karl had a nose for politics that allowed him to sense currents and to read people in a way that simply doesn't come from books. The area inside the beltway was densely packed with Ph.Ds., but some of those learned folks personified an unflattering definition of a Ph.D. as one who learns more and more about less and less until he knows everything about nothing.

Karl was a believer in special ops, a view he shared with Jack. They met frequently, enjoying what kids called good vibes and the professionals called trust and confidence. Karl solicited Jack's views, and Jack ran issues by Karl for what he called his "sanity check." Karl had a finely tuned shit detector. Jack never made an end run around his bosses via his access to the White House. That would have violated his sense of propriety.

But Jack didn't need end runs. The Army three-star Deputy Chief of Operations had been his battalion commander in the 82nd Airborne Division in The Big War, when Jack was a sharp platoon sergeant. Jack's company commander in Korea was now a general on the JCS Political-Military staff and, it was said, a man with a bright future. The point is that Jack was well wired, well liked, and disinclined to ask for special consideration. Insiders knew that when he took a position, he had thought it through and there was nothing in it for him personally. He never huffed and puffed, turned purple, or engaged in histrionics of any kind. His feelings ran deep. He was a pro, an insider with clout. Philosophers would call him the Good Man.

Karl, Jack, Mark Burns, and Pietro were different breeds of cats, but they shared respect for one another, affection for combat soldiers, and a conviction that special operations were a smart and cost effective way to use military force.

Saigon

Conway put down the telephone after his chat with the female major who worked with Colonel Plunkett in the JCS. He realized it was a gross military impropriety for him to undress the major—she sounded like a fine looking woman—but he did it anyway. His fertile imagination—he smiled at the thought of fertility—was probably making a silk purse out of a sow's ear. The truth, he confessed to himself, is that he wasn't actually focused on her imagined ear. Anyway, she would initiate the call from Washington to Saigon. The amazing Pentagon switchboard, when using the highest priority, could get Saigon, or anyplace else, almost immediately. Saigon switch did its best, but Conway wanted assurance that the important call wouldn't get screwed up by some new commo guy making noises about priority. Originating at 0700 hours Washington time, the call from Colonel Plunkett to Colonel Pietro would come in on the secure line at 2000 hours, local. Conway then made a similar arrangement with a Navy chief in the office of Colonel Burns in Hawaii. Unfortunately for Jerry's fantasy life, the chief was a male. After informing the colonel of the incoming calls, Jerry decided that it was past time to mosey down Rue Tu Do, to Mamma Bic's Bar. He was horny. He'd buy one of her lovelies a Saigon tea and nibble on an ear. It was time for a little R&R, if only for a few hours.

73

PJ's Tutorial

At the appointed time, PJ enjoyed a gin and tonic at Fred's villa and the company of his chief's three charming ladies. Then, the two men were delivered downtown with Fred providing a running commentary en route.

"This is Rue Tu Do, Saigon's Main Street. There's the Presidential Palace. That way leads to bars popular with U.S. troops. And here we are at the Hotel Caravel."

PJ exited and took in a finely appointed lobby, well-fed men, lovely women, and a chorus of Vietnamese, French and English voices.

In the awkward silence in the elevator, PJ played a private game. Noting that there is less conversation in an elevator than in church, he guessed that one Caucasian man was American, two were French, and the European woman was French. The others were Vietnamese.

His guesstimates were confirmed by the conversation that resumed as the elevator emptied into a first class restaurant, absolving the vow of silence. The short haircut spoke English to his girl. The men smoking the short, fat cigarettes spoke French to one another. The silent French woman was just indisputably French.

The maître d' greeted Fred with a smile of recognition, seating him and his guest at the table for two by the window that PJ would have selected, but not rated. Fred rated.

Looking down and then out to the horizon, PJ registered the lights and movement directly below, diminishing in intensity and slowing until they became quiet stars above where earth and sky met and black stillness reigned.

"Thank you, Fred."

"I thought you'd appreciate the view and the symbolism."

"The view is holiness spoiled. Man corrupts nature."

"Then he betrays his own species."

"Hmm. Metaphysics over cocktails."

"Yes, but first the food. It doesn't match the view, but it is excellent."

Civilized discourse and the fine meal were the overture to the magic show that followed.

"PJ, a Vietnamese officer once told me that we are here to make an

American Singapore of Cam Rahn Bay; that we are colonists; that we moved in as successors to the French. Cartesian logic demands reason. To make the world safe for democracy, to contain godless Communism simply don't wash. It isn't in the lexicon of the Vietnamese elites trained and educated by the French. Our claims are idealistic, fuzzy. Politics is about power, not poetry. Power allows you to get yourself and your family rich. That's the way the French and the Vietnamese understand our being here."

Cognac arrived, bringing silence as both men savored the pleasant warmth produced by one of man's truly noteworthy accomplishments.

"What's your general take on this war, PJ?"

There was no pause. PJ had cut his teeth on the Beatles, Ed Sullivan, JFK, LBJ, Goldwater, Nixon, SDS, BSU, Black Panthers, the burning of the Stanford NROTC building, the ransacking of the Stanford Research Institute, Berkley, Columbia, Kent State, pot, Janis Joplin.

"Dumber than most wars. Prolonging it harms all of us."

"Does it make a difference—mandarins, communists, or west oriented pols?"

"I don't think so. I believe in western liberal democracy, separation of powers, civil liberties, mother, and apple pie. I just don't believe my preferences are shared by many folks around the world."

"The citizens of Liberia, Bangladesh, and Armenia don't see things like the good folks of Des Moines?"

PJ laughed. "Hell, the good folks of Des Moines and Peoria don't see things like the their compatriots in Noo Yawk and LA."

"Are you offended by Zippos igniting thatched roofs, bombs in the north, the brutalization of soldiers...?"

"Yeah. God forgive me, that bothers me less than the pure stupidity of it, all of it. War brutalizes. It always has. Governments put the best face on screw-ups. Bureaucrats and government spokesmen say 'collateral damage,' as though words could make it something other than the killing of innocents. All of that comes from war—good wars and bad wars. But in this one we're stupidly engaged in a bad war. My government can't explain it and can't figure how to get out of it."

"That's a problem for all of us, most of all for your generation. I didn't have a crisis of conscience when I was a soldier in 'the Big One.' We didn't do it perfectly, but it needed doing. So we did it.

"Tell me, PJ, if not for your medical disqualification, would you have served in uniform in this 'stupid' war?"

"With gusto."

"How do you reconcile that with 'stupid' war?"

"Easily. Maybe that makes me a balanced schizoid...."

"My favorite type."

"I was at prep school when Kennedy made his inaugural address. Our teacher turned on the TV. When Kennedy finished we were ready to charge the nearest windmill. One of my schoolmates went to West Point and is now a Special Forces officer. Another is a Marine Corps officer. Several went south to register black voters. Several went to the Peace Corps. Some went to Canada, some are in the slammer, some in government, and some in the boondocks over here looking for the Medal of Honor."

"And," said Fred, "at least one is a budding journalist in Saigon."

"Yeah, I could have gone any route: Peace Corps or Marine Corps, register voters or ranger school. Kennedy told my generation to get out there and do something besides mow a lawn and paint a white picket fence in Levittown. We did."

PJ was distracted as diners moved to windows, and Fred got to his feet.

"Let's join the crowd."

Well fed, lubricated, and well dressed, the crowd watched a light show. In the distant darkness, tracers of green and orange could be seen but not heard. Then a faint thump-thump-thump of helicopters faded as the choppers flew to the tracers. The red lines of light from the aircraft intersected with the green lines from the ground. The silent movie lasted a few minutes. Viewers remained at the windows. Drinks were freshened to the murmuring in three languages. Fred listened to PJ.

"That's what you meant by betraying the species: fat cats taking pleasure in the spectacle as men die."

"Yes."

"Fred, I think you just told me to get out there to see for myself. You knew I would feel contempt for the bastards in this room."

"Did it work?"

"Where is the nearest windmill, Mr. Kennedy?"

CHAPTER FIVE

Decision: It's a Go

Saigon

Sergeant Conway announced that Colonel Burns was on the line from Hawaii. Coffee cup filled, yellow legal pad in the left oblique, a copy of the Fat Albert report between the cup and the pad: Colonel Pietro was ready for anything. Even Mark Burns.

"Mark, how come you're not on the beach next to a bikini?"

"Cuz you need a responsible adult to do the thinkin' for you killers."

"Before somebody preempts us, have you seen the Alabama report of a couple of hours ago, our area of interest?"

"Got it in front of me. Bin waitin' for your call."

The colonels should have used the secure phone, but they hated it. Voices sounded like Donald Duck talking in an echo chamber. Delays caused by scrambling and unscrambling the conversation on the encryption instrument caused speakers to interrupt one another as they took pauses to mean that the other person had completed his statement. So, security violations resulted from an aversion to using the telephone designed for passing classified information. The worst offenders were generals and old colonels, the same people who routinely misplaced classified documents and violated other security precautions. Because they didn't hear well, they played games on the ordinary telephone, routinely violating common sense and commo procedure.

"Mark, I knew you'd go for it. How about the admiral?"

"He'll go for it if you tie it to Vietnamization."

"That's it! That's my assumption!"

"Yeah. Pass the buck to our little brown brothers. The buzz from the DC head shed is to get out 'with honor.' They'll go for anything that accelerates the process."

"How about over the fence in force?"

"Our guys or conventional?"

"Our guys. Gotta allow denial if it turns to shit."

"Affirm. Don't go too light. If you got what I think you got, they'll come at you like mad bees. They'll try to roll over you."

There he goes, thought Pietro. I want authorization from pols, and Mark's already into tactical detail. Again.

"Yeah. I have a few ideas about that. Look, whisper in the admiral's ear. I want him on our side if the JCS or the pols ask for his views."

"No guarantee, but I think you can count on him. You know you can count on me."

"Thanks. We'll be talking. Out."

Pietro sighed. Before talking to Jack in Washington, he doodled on his yellow pad with a black felt tip pen.

Mark Burns immediately saw the strategic utility of the intel from Fat Albert's mission. Mark knew Pietro would want to close the choke point. That's what Mark would do. He also knew Pietro would need him and Jack to grease the skids. Mark didn't articulate like a grammarian, but there was nothing wrong with his mind. He liked to say that he hadn't much use for algebra, but his 'rithmetic was real good. He liked the nuts and bolts of operations.

Now to Jack; Pietro knew he had to put him in the picture early, so he didn't think he was the last one informed. The trouble is that once the idea appears on paper, every son of a bitch in Saigon, Hawaii, and

Washington will screw with it and try to make it his baby. Pietro knew he was gonna get a lot of advice. The fewer written words the better.

Pietro called out to Conway.

"Let's talk to Colonel Plunkett."

"Gotcha covered, sir. Laid it on. They initiate."

"One step ahead of me, as usual. No one preempts a JCS call."

"That's what I figured. Otherwise the PX Commander ordering Kotex pads would have a higher priority than you ordering something like a combat operation."

Pietro noodled and doodled as he waited, thinking to himself:

"Beef up SOG elements. Teams are light, trained, armed, and equipped for fast action and exfiltrate. Even heavy teams rarely carried weapons heavier than an M-60 machine gun. Don't need much more than big balls to tap a commo cable, conduct a recon, or grab a POW. Surprise, speed, and max air support gave recon its edge. It was similar for Exploitation Company. 'Heavy' meant extra machine guns. Maybe light mortars. The heavy shooting was done by air. When our teams got in their hair, the enemy concentrated to overwhelm the friendlies. That's when air came on the scene—if all went well—to nail the bunched up NVA as our guys broke contact. Shoot and scoot, but to dig in and stay on the trail for 3 or 4 days? Gotta be ready for the enemy's first team to arrive. Then bring the U.S. Air Force in, like the U.S. Cavalry in a John Wayne film. But we don't have skyhooks to keep the birds constantly over us in a denied area. Guys in a blocking position will have their butts hanging out in a place owned by Uncle Ho, especially if the weather turned shitty. Not unlikely in the tri-border area."

Pietro picked away at it:

"If this plays out the way it should, NVA commanders will pour max resources into destroying us. Hanoi can't tolerate interruption of the flow men and supplies to the south, especially now that they smell victory. They'll come at us with all they've got. Expect automatic weapons on wheeled vehicles. Maybe tracks. Maybe light tanks. PT-76s are in the neighborhood. Look into weapons light in weight with punch able to bust up tanks. That would surprise an enemy expecting no more than the usual recon team's small arms. Could spoil their whole day. Fry their ass. We have good stuff in the SOG warehouse, WWII stuff available and expendable. Hell, it was expendable in 1945. Use it. Destroy in place if we can't take it out under enemy pressure. Drop a thermite grenade down the tube and melt the mother. No big deal. Shit. If not destroyed, the weapons and ammo would wind up in some bazaar in the Middle East, Kabul, Belfast, Africa or some other dust up, probably to be aimed at us someplace.

Conway broke Pietro's train of thought.

"Sir, Washington on the line; Colonel Plunkett."

Pietro pushed his yellow pad toward Conway. It said:

"Jerry, re: blocking force. How big? Maximum size of force acceptable to political authority? How many U.S.? How many total? How do we get in? B-52 strike? Enemy tanks reported in area. Beef up. How? Maybe stuff too heavy to man-carry: land, use & destroy. Get ideas of weapons guys. Need redundant commo & recognition signals for Air Force, day & night. What AF gun ships available at night? Engineer equipment for hasty fortification: sandbags, wire, stakes, explosives, chain saws, etc. Planned stay time 3,4,5 days? Can big chopper carry small bulldozer? Earthmover? Estimate enemy reaction: How fast? How strong? Include doctor + how many medics? Augment RTs supporting blocking force? Where near main trail? Force organization, non-standard weapons/equipment. MISSION: Put bad hurt on enemy logistics to support Vietnamization."

His last entry was a smiling face, the kind that goes with Have A Nice Day!

Jerry nodded affirm to his colonel's note. Gotcha. Consult good guys re: practical stuff. Shape plan.

"Later," said Pietro, nodding to Jerry, with his hand over the phone's mouthpiece. Then, into the phone:

"How's life in the Puzzle Palace, Jack?"

Jack Plunkett knew that his friend was interested in the political climate, not the weather or gossip.

To Jack the meaning of Fat Albert's mission leaped from the page. Bingo! This late in the game an RT found a key choke point on the enemy's main supply route in Laos, the trail from North Vietnam to various entry points into South Vietnam.

"Too bad we didn't find it earlier, when we were still trying to win the war," thought Jack. Ironic. When the United States was still serious about winning the war, instead of focusing on how to get out "with honor," a cross-border operation of the magnitude he contemplated would have been regarded as the fantasy of some dullard in uniform. Even dumb soldiers understood that concern for Chinese intervention—as in Korea in 1950—dictated caution regarding American cross-border operations. And world opinion says play nice.

How ironic. The enemy played the game as if the international borders recognized in Paris in 1954 didn't exist or didn't matter in the real world: Indo-China was Indo-China. The U.S. played the game as if Laos, Cambodia and Vietnam were sovereign states, not fake constructs. Then we violated the rules as our soldiers fought their soldiers where neither admitted being there. We do make it hard on ourselves.

The enemy used non-belligerent countries, Laos and Cambodia, for transit and storage of military materiel. The U.S. had to be discreet in its use of small teams in those non-belligerent neighbor countries over the fence from Vietnam. But now that the U.S. simply wanted out, without too much egg on its face, a bold incursion into Laos might be acceptable. Finally, American military leadership had figured it out: U.S. policy considerations, not tactical or operational considerations, were paramount. A dozen years after the "police action" in Korea, it dawned on some soldiers at the top that war was a political act—and military service required officers to study. Short hair, shined jump boots and willing young troopers were not enough. Thinking was authorized.

Jack's voice cut into Pietro's ruminations.

"You know how it goes. Get here in the dark and leave in the dark. From my windowless perch, damned if I know if it's rain or shine."

"The White House and State Department believe that the Pentagon is always in the dark."

"Yes. And to make it more fun, they are excavating for a metro stop right here. That knocks out about 400 parking places. I park a mile from The Building. You see, we have improved paradise since you left."

The good things about assignment to the Pentagon were few: the schools in northern Virginia, theater in town, and the job. Many of the jobs were inherently interesting, and even officers unhappy about assignment to Washington realized that their planning affected millions of people. Everything else, especially the basic stuff like commuting to work and paying rent, was bad. A Pentagon joke was that an entire floor should be closed down some morning to see how long it would take before anyone outside noticed. Most officers looked forward to an assignment in the Pentagon about the way a ten-year old boy anticipated returning to school after summer vacation.

"Roger, how can I help you?"

"Did you see what Fat Albert turned up?"

"Yes. But we're not secure. Is that the subject?"

"Affirm. Tell me if this is the time to do it."

Plunkett paused. He wanted to be precise.

"Timing is good. The atmosphere here is conducive to any course of action that hands the war to Saigon and gets us out sooner rather than later."

Pietro added "looks good in DC" to "looks good in PAC" plus two smiley faces in his constantly handy yellow pad.

"Thanks Jack. Mark sees it that way. He thinks his boss will go for it. I can tell my boss that we can begin planning. What restrictions or limitations will come down? Assume it's a 'go.' What strings will be attached?"

Jack didn't want to build false hopes, but he sensed that in DC the time was ripe for approving the mission taking shape in Pietro's head.

"Restrictions would be something like this..."

He paused, thinking.

"Deniability; short stay time over the fence; minimum number of U.S. personnel; minimum size of total force. I stress plausible deniability."

"Jack, how long need we stay to hurt enough to justify effort? Are you tracking?"

"Yes. Understand. You need a basis for planning. I'll put it to my boss."

This much was stated or implied: deniable, few U.S., small footprint, no paper trail.

"Roger. Prez trusts Mark's squid. He's the key to a go ahead."

Clear text: If the admiral approves, the president will probably buy it.

"Thanks. Be back to you. Get us a thumbs up."

"You get my best shot. Out."

Jack was gone.

As soon as he hung up, Pietro added to his cryptic who-does-what and what-do-we-need memo for Jerry. His to-do list emphasized:

#1 is plausible deniability.
Then:
Minimum number of U.S. troops.
Smallest total force to get job done.
How long stay time in Laos?
What is our best package of people and things?
Think through total air support required.
Brief mission to SOG boss to get his concurrence.
Back to Mark and Jack for PACOM and JCS approval.
Recommend when to execute.
When give warning order to CCC?
MUM'S THE WORD!

His heart thumped, and he noticed that the hand that had held the phone was wet with sweat. He was a happy soldier. What his brain trust in Saigon had come up with was about right. He felt vindicated that Mark in Hawaii and Jack in Washington reacted positively. But another thought flitted through his mind: If a half-million American troops couldn't whip Hanoi, how could upgefucked Saigon? He kicked that doubt out of his consciousness. His job was to buy time for Vietnamization. That was national policy. Salute. Execute. Carry out that policy.

"Jerry!"

Conway had been studying Pietro's first memo in preparation for this summons and had done his own doodling. Old fire horses and old operations types are wired for rapid response. Sound the fire alarm; see the alerted beast eager to go. Mention combat operations; see the salivating operations type noodle and doodle.

"Sir?"

"Jerry, it's 'looks good.'"

"Sir, it sure makes a difference to deal with real soldiers instead of cookie pushers. What can I do?"

"Could you decipher my notes? See what I mean about clout?"

"Yessir, but when we say minimal total force and minimal U.S. personnel, what's our ballpark estimate of what we'll need? And when do we tell CCC?"

Pietro paused.

"Let's figure a total force of some 250 troops. Say 50 U.S. Say CCC's Exploitation Company of about 150 men plus ten RTs organized into ten-man Hatchet Teams. There's 250. Figure three U.S. per Hatchet Team and about twenty with the company. That's 30 plus 20 for 50 U.S."

He was doing his 'rithmetic on a pad as he spoke.

"We don't tell CCC until we have approval. The recon men get around. They'll leak it if there's much time between the warning order and insertion. Besides, I don't want to get their hopes up. It's not in the bag yet."

"Sir, once we give them the mission, we set up an isolation area in Kontum and keep them there for their own good."

"Right. Close hold. If the boss blesses it, we set up a planning cell here. What else?"

"I'll rough out organization—people, weapons and equipment—and show it to you. Once approved, do we bring CCC here, or do we go to Kontum? Then we finalize organization of the force, heavy it up, and let CCC prepare to do the job.

"Think this one through: How much time will CCC need to come up with a detailed plan, rehearse, integrate some heavy weapons, and do specific mission training? Once we pick a D-day, we'll back off to give CCC the order and time for mission prep."

"Got it, sir. Couldn't we bring CCC into it now? They'd have a better feel for how much time they need. I'd also like to talk weapons augmentation with some of the old guys."

"No! Security is critical. Young tigers talk too much."

"Understand."

"But we give Air Force a warning order, a 'be prepared to...' with max time. They'll have to surge for our op since it comes on top of all their other missions in country and up north. They are absolutely key. The way I see it, we stack up the enemy and Air Force kills him. This thing will be coming down from the President, SECDEF, and JCS. Shouldn't be doubt about priority. Meanwhile we give CCC just enough time for planning and prep so they can't talk about the mission from here to hell and back."

Pietro now had to sell the mission to his boss, the SOG Chief, who would present it to the U.S. general commanding in Vietnam.

Jerry laughed, saying to the colonel:

"Sir, ain't we like two kids in a candy store?"

"Yeah! I admit I'm charged!"

Now they were both laughing at one another and at themselves.

***

Pietro's session with the boss went well. Long experience in intelligence and psychological operations had fine-tuned the Chief's political antenna, also known as his shit detector. And his duties had regularly brought him into contact with political movers and shakers. His reaction to Pietro's scheme was a carbon copy of Jack's and Mark's. He liked it. The SOG chief determined on the spot to recommend the blocking force mission to the cigar-chomping four-star hero of WWII now commanding all U.S. troops in the RVN.

***

The impulse to strike a hard blow in order to buy time for the Saigon government seemed as necessary to Abe as the whack on the baby's ass to get his lungs cleared. He listened quietly to his MACVSOG Chief. Then he was curt.

"I like the concept. The message you drafted for me to approve will be on its way to the Chairman and PACOM within the hour. I'll notify you as soon as we have a response. Continue planning. Keep me informed. Good work."

That was about as effusive as the old tanker got. The decision-making process Pietro had so often criticized as cumbersome and sluggish was working well. Higher headquarters he'd accused of being ribbon clerks was decisive. The confluence of Vietnamization and the information from Fat Albert's last recon mission stimulated the operators and made the decision easy—in Saigon.

Mark and Commander-in-Chief, Pacific

Mark Burns made his move at the CINCPAC daily staff conference. As Mark concluded his portion of the briefing, the admiral posed a question bearing on enemy resupply rates. The admiral's logistics question was stimulated by the heavy flow of communications traffic from Washington concerning Vietnamization and how the Vietnamese would manage in the absence of American forces. That was just the opening Mark was looking for.

"Admiral, I need to meet with you privately on a related matter."

Turning to his executive officer, the keeper of a full appointments schedule, the admiral said:

"Get Mark in to see me soonest."

The relationship between the rough-hewn colonel and the acerbic and sophisticated admiral had warmed to a degree that surprised veterans of the admiral's staff. As the staff left the conference room, the XO gave Burns the time for his session with CINCPAC.

***

In the privacy of the admiral's office, Mark made his pitch for Pietro's plan. He spelled out the significance of the RT's discovery of the choke point, MACVSOG's desire to block the trail to create a killing ground, and the connection to Vietnamization. The admiral listened.

"How long must that force remain in Laos?"

"Sir, we think in three or four days we could inflict a high order of damage."

87

The admiral frowned.

"We are doing a cost/benefit analysis. The cost is loss of life, possible loss of U.S. prestige, possible embarrassment to the administration. That's a way to say that the President is being asked to stick his neck out. He has an election to think about. He'll want to know what he gets for the cost. I know it's tough to quantify, but we must set up the equation. 'A high order of damage' just won't get it. We need to give the President and his National Security Advisor something they can sink their teeth into."

The admiral walked to the chalkboard he maintained in every office he had occupied from the day he got his first desk. He turned to gaze out the window for a minute. Mark shifted from one foot to the other. The admiral stared at the chalkboard. Then he started to write. The messy chalk and chalk dust of schoolboy days had been replaced by neat dry ink, and the schoolboy was now a powerful man.

He stepped back to study his handiwork.

POSSIBLE COST vs POSSIBLE GAIN
- Lives vs time for RVN
- Defeat vs early out for U.S. troops
- Prestige vs hurt enemy

After a minute or two of studying the lists, the admiral spoke.

"Worst case, we lose some fifty U.S. military. Nobody in Washington cares about 200 dead mercenaries. Truth is, fifty U.S. dead won't worry them much either, unless the story turns up on the front page of the Post, Journal, or Times. ORSA guys do policy formulation in quantitative terms, inputs and outputs, like plant managers. In the White House war room, war is a bloodless affair."

The admiral paused. He seemed to be reflecting on the words he had just uttered, as though he was thinking aloud. No one ever raised the subject in his presence, but the staff was constantly aware that his son, a naval aviator, had been a prisoner of war for the past three years. Enemy treatment of captured American pilots was brutal. The veteran of sea combat in World War II and Korea knew that war was a bloody affair. He also knew that the Hanoi Hilton was not a nice place.

CINCPAC went on, for his audience of one.

"Since the NVA will continue to use the trail in Laos after the U.S. is out of Vietnam, it is unlikely that Hanoi will publicize the battle. To do so would raise the question of what the hell the NVA is doing in Laos. So the maximum cost is the 50 U.S. lives. Are you with me?"

"Yes, sir. The propaganda value to the enemy is less than the operational value of the resupply routes in Laos."

The old salt paused as he stared at Mark.

"I couldn't say it better. We could make a numbers cruncher out of you. With work and application you might qualify for the United States Navy."

The admiral turned back to the board.

"On the profit side of the ledger, interruption of the resupply supports the President's policy: Get out of Vietnam without a messy collapse of Saigon."

"Admiral, you left out something important."

"What's that?"

"Somebody in Washington might give a shit if the 50 U.S. were draftees, but there won't be much heartburn if volunteers die."

"You're catching on, Mark. That's right. That's why they hired us."

"Sir, seen this way, the exact amount of time we buy for the Saigon government is less important than the high probability that we buy some time at relatively low cost."

"Agree. That's my opinion. I endorse the concept."

"My friends in special ops will be pleased to hear that."

"Be discreet. I wouldn't want the President to think he was the last one to know my opinion."

"Yes, sir."

"Packaging is important. The president is surrounded by number-crunchers. Your people on the JCS staff know how to task the intel community, but let's help them. Tell them we want the daily throughput on the trail based on current intel and their holdings on enemy logistics. Then it's a simple multiplication. Throughput per day, times days, times estimate of percent of damage. Still with me?"

"Yes, sir." Mark was taking notes.

"The last is an educated guess, but do it anyway. Mr. McNamara taught us that even crude numbers are more convincing to an official audience than the best prose or poetry. Numbers are to today's society what indulgences, incense, and Gregorian chant were to the Middle Ages. Use contemporary religion, Mark. Estimate of damage inflicted can be interpolated to an estimate of time. The NVA will need to make up for the hell your people raise on the trail. Say it in numbers. Say it in tons and time. Count up the indulgences."

"Sir, DIA and CIA have invested a lot of resources in the NVA infiltration into Vietnam. They have estimates already on hand."

"So much the better. Don't piecemeal. Lay it out. That helps in the decision process. It also saves me time."

"Yes, sir," said the chastened colonel in a little boy voice as he saluted and did a smart about-face. Mark had learned how to get in the last word when dealing with authority. It was, "Yes, ma'am"—or an equivalent.

***

Mark grabbed a cup of coffee and scratched out a few notes at his desk before calling Jack Plunkett to task the intel community to assess the effects on the enemy of choking off resupply for two days, for three days, for four days, and for five days.

He was chastened—for the second time in an hour—this time by Jack's response. "Good idea, Mark. I did that. Intel analysts have been working the problem intensely since 1964. Each day our guys block the trail costs Hanoi about a week to make up losses. That's a gross estimate. Critical items could take months to replace. You never know what's in the back of a truck we blow up."

Mark was disappointed in himself for not being as quick as Jack and the admiral. They often get to the essence immediately; Mark had to double-clutch. But he got there.

"OK, Jack. It's up to you to sell it to The Man."

"Well, first to the Chairman and SECDEF. As soon as P sends me details, I'll make my play. Your admiral's views matter one hell of a lot to the President."

"Good. Be careful how you use his name. I don't want to damage the President's trust in my boss. Thanks for your help. Out."

Skull Sessions in High Places

Things were moving quickly, thought Jack Plunkett as he looked at the brevity code Pietro had gotten to him in his own ingenious way. Tucked away in the daily weather forecast from the Air Force in Saigon—a long report filled with abbreviations, alpha and numeric codes for winds at various altitudes, visibility, precipitation, temperatures, probabilities, percentages, and gibberish essential to operations—was a single line for Jack: "a. 250 b. 50 c. wilco d. affirm e. 4/5." The line preceding this message for Jack was deliberately garbled, the key that said, "What follows is our brevity code." It stated the total number, number of U.S., intent to get out quickly, deniability, and expected stay time in Laos.

Before initiating a call to Saigon, Jack ran the entire scenario through to himself, one more time:

"A couple of things are still missing. I cannot ask my pal to have the President make yet another tough call about the war. LBJ is a private citizen on his ranch in Texas because of the Vietnam millstone. His successor likes the address and intends to renew his lease in 1972.

"How do we prep the objective area before inserting the ground force? B-52 strikes? Can a light SOG force be sustained for 4-5 days against a pissed off NVA battalion? Regiment? Air assets are no problem, if the mission were a go."

One of the jollies of serving on the JCS staff is power. Simply uttering: "This is Colonel Plunkett, Special Ops, JCS," was usually enough to get the undivided attention of the person on the other end of the line, even if that person wore stars on his collar. Jack had been very discreet in using his big stick. The only bigger stick was a call from the White House or SECDEF. Jack never rubbed in the fact that he had more clout than most of the people wearing stars. When he had to lean on people, they assumed he was working something hot. This was hot. "We just tell the Air Force that this mission has priority over everything else for as long as CCC's blocking force is in Laos," he thought. The "we" being the Chairman of the JCS. That's that.

He called Pietro.

***

Jack learned that Pietro planned an Arc Light, a B-52 strike, on the trail. After the strike, CCC elements would land right on the objective. The torn up terrain would ease the clearing of fields of fire and provide construction materials for hasty fortifications. Priority for air was to SOG. Fortifications. Barriers. Anti-tank weapons. OK. The American commander in Vietnam buys it. So does the President's man in the Pacific, CINCPAC. So does the top man in uniform, the Chairman, JCS. Intel says four days of choking the trail in Laos will cost the bad guys four weeks to catch up. The assumption is that the enemy must stockpile a heap of goodies, chiefly munitions, before he can sustain an offensive. This hurts him. This helps our little brown brothers.

"Let's nail it down," thought Plunkett. "Short and sweet. I'll run it by Karl for his blessing and any adjustments he proposes. Karl might brief it to the President. His boss, the Metternich of the White House, might lay it out for the President. They might want me to do it. Or the Chairman. Hell, whatever Karl says.

"What have I overlooked?"

From the nitty-gritty details of a recon team's activity to the sophisticated show and tell at the top of the pol-mil pecking order, Jack tied it down in a short paper. Not many officials were as comfortable as Jack with the full range of the use of force from minor tactics, through operations, military strategy, national strategy, and national policy.

Karl knew the personalities at the top, and perhaps most importantly, he knew how to package and present the scheme for that audience. Personalities may trump analysis. So might other issues on the president's plate that seemed more pressing to him. The Commander in Chief might give this matter as much as two minutes before turning to another on a list of issues demanding his attention. Jack reminded himself of what he never tired of telling younger officers: be brief, be right, and be gone. Jack reached for the phone to call Karl. Whatever Karl says.

***

Karl invited Jack to his corner in the White House. They could have discussed their business at the Pentagon, but Karl didn't want Jack to be tense should there be an audience with the President. Let him find his way around the White House and discover that the working stiffs there weren't very different from the stiffs at DOD, CIA, State, a think tank, or the faculty of a university. In fact, most of the staffers at the National Security Council came from just such places, the same manpower pool. Despite Jack's intelligence, sophistication and background of privilege, his military socialization inclined him to respect for the office of the President that came close to reverence. His Commander in Chief might be a saint or a son of a bitch, but he was the Commander in Chief. The American people said so.

Karl greeted Jack, put a cup of coffee in front of him, and said: "Let's do it."

Jack handed him the paper. Karl read it and nodded.

"Good. It needs doing. Let's package the presentation. Reduce the prose to a point paper. That's the preferred way here. I'll give a copy of the point paper to Herr Doktor K. He'll tell me who will present it to the President for decision. I'm guessing that you will. The President prefers answers from the guy who presented, not from some expert backbencher. That's why I think you'll do it. No one else would want to show his ignorance if the president presses with questions of tactics or operations."

Jack nodded and said:

"I'll have the point paper to you ten minutes, if you lend me one of your super secretaries."

"You got it."

"I say back for possible correction: Point paper to you. You run with it. I might brief the scheme to the President. The words I wrote are appropriate for the brief."

"Affirmative."

"Venture a guess. Will he buy it?"

Without pausing, Karl said:

"I think so. You put your finger on it from the beginning. The hot button right now is to beef up the Government of RVN and its Army so that we can get out with what passes for honor. This President said in 1968 that he would get us out. It's time. My guess is your operation is a go."

"Time for me to get cracking. You must have pencils to sharpen or whatever it is you do around here. Call me if the nation is in trouble."

Karl grunted mock assent.

In twenty minutes he had the point paper.

***

Later, at home base, Jack recalled the German adage: Selbstlob stinkt. Self-praise stinks. But the general who ran the JCS staff had been explicit: He ordered Jack to tell the assembled officers of the section, chapter and verse, how it went. His officers should know what they might expect if they were called by the White House to brief the President. What Jack described was also useful for the officers who would brief the JCS in "the tank," the secure room where the Service Chiefs met in the Pentagon. Modesty aside, Jack described for his colleagues what happened when he briefed the President of the United States in the White House. Big boy show and tell.

The favorable outcome in the White House had more to do with the President's needs than with Jack's skill, but the news was good.

On Pietro's yellow pad, authorization looked this way:

> Karl told Jack = White House to JCS
> Jack told Mark = JCS to CINCPAC
> Mark told Pietro = CINCPAC to MACVSOG
> Pietro told Radich = SOG to CCC

At the bottom of the pad, he printed in bold letters:

POETRY BECOMES PROSE!

The blocking force was a go.

PJ Makes Friends

PJ eased onto the bar stool, mellow before his first drink. In fact, he was walking on air. He was getting smart about the country, the war, journalism and the city. His piece on replacements going to war, heavily edited, had made it into Fred's weekly summary as: IF

VIETNAMIZATION, WHY REPLACEMENTS? He didn't get a by-line, but his name appeared after "with," as in "by Fred Wolf with Ed Fitzgerald in New York and PJ Riley in Saigon." First time at bat in the big leagues and he came up with a hit that knocked in a run. Family, friends, and teachers read the piece by war correspondent PJ Riley.

Glancing around the bar, he recognized none of the customers, but the B-girls were the usual cast. He was there for the bantering companionship of other young men and to learn about the military subculture that was his beat. The girls had to do what they had to do: hustle customers.

"Hey, PJ, you buy me Saigon tea?"

The B-girl bumped her hip against PJ's and rested her hand on his knee as her profoundly bored eyes looked through him. It might be drugs that deadened her eyes. Maybe it was hate.

"No can do."

She remained with him at the bar, a waste of her time to linger, but business was slow. It would pick up later as booze reduced inhibitions, and young men got hornier.

"You cheap charie, PJ. Buy drink for working girl."

She slid her hand from his knee to his vital parts.

"I send all money to my wife and children in the States."

"You bullshit, PJ. You no have wife. You have children?"

She pronounced it "chiren."

She giggled at her little joke as PJ speculated that boredom was the best part of her job. Can't be a hell of a lot of fun for the tiny woman under grunting, hairy big-noses who were too big for her in every way and usually at least a little drunk and trying too vigorously.

She gave it one more half-hearted try. "C'mon, PJ. I love you too much."

"Sin loi. I have bad sickness. No can do. Make you sick."

"Bullshit. You no sick. You cherry boy. What sick?"

"No bullshit. Doctor say bent-penis-itis. Make you die."

"Bullshit, cheap charie."

Charlie was pronounced char-rie by every bargirl in Vietnam. There might be an Ingrish for B-Girls Dictionary.

She moved down the bar to the next customer, avoiding a big loudmouth already drunk. He was with two men, not as big, not as drunk.

PJ, a quick read, had broken some codes in his new universe. He hadn't realized that there were so many Americans in country chasing a buck. The fat older Caucasians were mostly construction or communications contractors on permanent boys-night-out, a type unknown in World War II and Korea. Can't tell your players without a scorecard. Long hair, suit and tie was Frenchman; short hair was soldier; boorish was this clown.

"Hey, you. Take that little girl upstairs. Least buy her a drink."

PJ ignored the lout.

"Hey, pussy. You hear me?"

PJ felt the call of the wild, but he was cool. He didn't acknowledge the big drunk's existence, but he heard the scraping of a bar stool and the sound of Paul Bunyan hauling his bulk in PJ's direction. He smelled the breath of the big son of a bitch about the same time their eyes met at a range of one foot as the goon steadied himself with one hand on the bar and the other on the back of PJ's bar stool, his chest brushing PJ's shoulder.

"You hear me?"

PJ thought, "When he touches me with one of those paws, school's out. No point talking to a shithead determined to hit somebody. Me."

The big man guessed wrong. PJ was young, fit, and good at this kind of encounter. His concern was for the two guys backing up the jerk.

Phase one was over in five seconds; phase two was a happy surprise.

The jerk pushed a finger in PJ's chest, and that was the last thing he remembered when his friends revived him in a cab.

PJ's strength as a soccer player was his head ball, a shot that began with the delivery of his hairline to the moving ball. How much easier was the smashing of the oaf's nose with the old head ball shot, the kick delivered deliberately to the groin, and the surgical blow to the Adam's apple. PJ wheeled to address the reinforcements, but they were facing the bar with two strangers attached to them. The strangers in civilian dress had the arms of the reinforcements in awkward and uncomfortable positions. As the man on the barroom floor vomited, PJ heard one of his benefactors issuing careful instructions in a well-modulated voice to the puker's companions.

"Be smart. Help your buddy up. Be gone. Delay and we'll stomp you bad."

The bodies were propelled in the direction of the big jerk.

Evidence of their mature good judgment was manifest in the manner with which they gathered up the sorry sack of shit and half-carried him from the premises.

PJ addressed his reinforcements: "I owe you good Samaritans a drink. I'm PJ."

"Make mine a San Miguel," said one as he approached PJ with hand extended. "My name's Mike Schaefer."

"Dewars for me," said the other, smiling as he shook PJ's hand. "I'm Chuck. You do efficient work for a civilian twit."

"Thanks. I owe you guys."

Mike responded:

"We saw the deal shaping up. The big guy was cruisin' for a bruisin' before you arrived. The other two thought they had to back the asshole or lose face on the job. As they retell the story they'll have themselves kickin' ass and takin' names. Glad we could help."

"Yep," said Chuck. "De oppresso liber."

"Day what?"

"I'm being a wiseass. The SF motto is de oppresso liber, to free from oppression."

"So you two are Special Forces guys on a little R and R in Saigon?"

"Roger. A few days stand down. How about you?"

"I'm the gentleman of the press you've heard about."

"You must be the only one," Chuck observed.

"That's true. Quick physical reaction can't fully excuse his line of work," said Mike, "but it is mitigating. Most journalists couldn't get out of their own way."

"Listen," said PJ, warming to his new acquaintances and surprised at the repartee that was more Stanford campus than GI gin mill. "My hooch isn't far from here. Unless you have other plans for tonight, let's take it to my place. I'd like to talk to real soldiers."

Mike and Chuck exchanged glances. Chuck said:

"Suits me. I'd like to swap yarns with this feller."

"Roger that," Mike asserted. "It's also good tactics. Those a-holes might be dumb enough to come back with an AK or grenades to spoil our peaceful stay in sin city."

They adjourned to PJ's digs to drink and talk, establishing friendship before it became something else.

Later, dozing off, PJ was happy. War correspondent! Make that recently published war correspondent! Bar fighter! Make that victorious bar fighter! Drinking buddy of the foes of oppression! Visions of sugarplums danced in his brain. His next task would be to get out of Saigon to the boonies. His new friends had given him some tips. Soon he would experience war up close and personal. The prospect attracted him as it has attracted some young men for a long time. He was an enthusiastic apprentice. His new friends played in Saigon but had honed their skills in the field. Kontum was home, but their craft took them over the fence to their workbench in Laos. On operations they were independent Meisters. In Kontum they shared the fellow feeling of skilled artisans, members of a guild. A Saigon apprentice was not yet a member of the guild.

CHAPTER SIX

CCC, Kontum

Boonies and Bugs

Kontum City, in the central highlands of Kontum Province, sat on the narrow waist of the country, where, according to intelligence, the enemy intended to split the Republic of Vietnam into two parts before defeating each in detail. It was located on an infiltration route from the tri-border area, where Vietnam, Laos and Cambodia meet, to the South China Sea. The Ho Chi Minh trail ran south from North Vietnam on the Laotian side of the border, entering South Vietnam at various places, including trails west of Kontum.

Military jargon described the terrain as difficult, which was rather like describing the Pacific Ocean as a salty pond. The real estate on both sides of the unmarked border was indistinguishable, mostly mountains; in part dense jungle of triple canopy where it was always twilight and dank, even at midday; in part by forests like those along the Appalachian Trail in the United States; in part by thickets of bamboo through which a combat-loaded soldier wedged himself with some difficulty as splinters cut like tiny knives; in part by razor sharp holly bushes that tore skin and fabric; in part by wait-a-minute vines that grabbed the weapons, canteens, ammo pockets and scabbards of very weary soldiers, as though saying, not so fast; and in part by fields of tall, sharp elephant grass. The Appalachian-like forest, plentiful in the Central Highlands, was the part most familiar and congenial to Americans.

Disused and uninhabited French plantations were stumbled upon, eliciting the creepy feeling of entering a house without the owner's permission. Cultivation was losing its struggle with the jungle, but the land continued to produce some delicious fruit to be consumed on a rest break. A glance around a plantation revealed a once-upon-a-time paradise. Mountain streams and white waterfalls lulled the viewer with bucolic sights and murmuring sounds. A soldier could forget for a moment the violent purpose of his presence there.

Chilly nights, hinting early October in Pennsylvania, belied the stereotypical image of sweltering jungle. But plantations and cool nights would be forgotten in the sweaty exertion of the day as the sun melted men. Monsoon rains chilled bodies soaked with sweat for an hour or two before the sun returned to create an enervating steam bath as clothing dried. The always present for duty jungle vines and thorns grabbed and cut tired bodies. Wet and hot by day, troops shivered at night.

Special dispensation granted by Asian gods and Christian bishops ensured that thoughts remained private intellectual property. Bedding down for delicious rest that might last for minutes or hours, dreams beamed optimists from a bad to a good place—and relegated pessimists to nocturnal discomfort.

Homo sapiens, of brown and white persuasions, were but one form of animal life in the bush over the fence, one of many. God has a sense of humor. Or was he testing Job again? The least of His creatures were the large ones commonly believed to be menacing: elephants, tigers, cobras, and water buffalo gone feral. In fact, critters got field soldiers' attention in inverse proportion to their size. Small bamboo vipers got more attention than cobras. Concern for red ants dwarfed—pun intended—concern for elephants, particularly when a soldier settled in the dark to share a chunk of God's earth with an unseen mound of red ants. Leeches are blood-sucking beasties; mosquitos carried several strains of malaria; and other little uglies repelled: microscopic bugs causing dysentery or diarrhea were possible contenders with the red ant for Champion Nemesis of the American Field Soldier. But the red ant was probably the champion pest to soldiers taking temporary residence in his domain.

Day's Take

Major Day, the Crazy Major, was keenly aware of the changeable weather, difficult terrain, and God's creatures inhabiting the north-south Central Highlands that were western Vietnam and eastern Laos. The border was both unmarked and unobserved by aboriginals and current combatants. He knew from personal experience the physical discomfort and psychological challenge of simply walking and surviving in that setting, compounded by the awareness of being on the home turf of an unseen enemy never far away. "Yet," he mused, "we never lacked volunteers to take on the RT missions, even as growing numbers of their peers in the United States demonstrated against the war in Vietnam."

He believed the men of CCC were held together by both mutual respect from kindred souls and the pure adventure of cross-border operations against a worthy enemy whose intent was to kill them. In his late thirties, Day was a decade older than his soldiers who used guile, skills and courage in jungle duels. He sent them to bad places to do difficult tasks. A veteran of the war in Korea and on a second tour in Vietnam, he saw himself as an uncle to his warriors. The more perspicacious of the shooters recognized him as their guardian angel. Others saw him as another link in a chain of quill-pushers in safe places, one of the functionaries field soldiers relegate to the ranks of clerks and jerks who handle the gear in the rear—a pain in the ass. Brits have The Regiment; Aussies have Mates; Germans have Kameraden; GIs have Buddies. All are exclusive fraternities, as was CCC.

The Latch-up

Home for Sergeant Grady, Major Day and 100 American Special
Forces soldiers was the CCC camp they shared with 1,000 indigenous
mercenaries recruited, trained, paid and led by Americans. Nominally
commanded by a Vietnamese lieutenant colonel, the de facto boss
of was Lieutenant Colonel Radich. He controlled what mattered:
money, supplies, and fire support. The mercenaries were Vietnamese,
Montagnards and Chinese, with a sprinkling of other ethnic and
religious groups in various shades of skin color. It was organized into
three companies: Security, Reconnaissance, and Exploitation. Recon
was further organized into teams named for states, as in RT California,
RT Montana, RT West Virginia. The Recon Teams typically consisted
of three Americans and ten to twelve indigenous mercenaries. Some
team leaders were inclined to go light, taking as few as two Americans
and two mercenaries. Others preferred to go heavy, with as many as
three Americans and nine mercenaries. The assigned mission was the
overriding consideration; the team leader determined how many men
were required for a specific job. The decision was his.

The operating principle was simple: give the team leader the
mission; let him figure out the how of it; listen to his brief-back; then
ask your questions.

Rule-of-thumb was six combat loaded soldiers per helicopter. By
CCC standards, four men was a light insertion, one helicopter load.
Twelve men was heavy, two choppers.

Exploitation Company consisted of about a hundred men organized
into three platoons. Squad leaders, platoon sergeants, platoon leaders,
first sergeant and company commander were Americans. There was an
indigenous chain of command that took its orders from Americans.
Seldom was the whole company committed to a single operation.
Usually platoon size elements of some thirty men were employed to
raid and ambush. A recon team or a squad might be inserted to rescue
a downed pilot or recover his body.

Security Company controlled access to the camp and restricted
area, such as the Tactical Operation Center. On the perimeter of the
camp were barbed wire, mines, bunkers and trenches. Mortar pits

dotted the inside of the camp. The Americans and mercenaries of the Security Company guarded the camp, day and night. At times of expected trouble, everyone in camp defended home and hearth.

The Men

Major Day's sleeping area was much smaller than a college freshman's dorm room, but by CCC standards it was the Waldorf Astoria. It afforded privacy. The cinder block appendage to a larger structure was six feet from the trench and bunker line that surrounded the camp. Inside, it measured some ten by ten feet. Furnishings consisted of a standard GI metal bed with camouflaged poncho liner serving as bedspread, footlocker (with his name, rank and serial number in white paint), folding chair, field desk and a wall-locker, all GI, all green. Improbably in the austere setting, it had a sink with running water. A shotgun, an M-16 and a gas mask hung on one wall. His flack jacket, a protective vest, hung on the folding chair along with the web gear that carried two canteens, ammo pouches, survival kit, knife, compass, and smoke grenades required in the bush. Pictures of his wife and son stood on the footlocker that served as night table, coffee table and extra seat.

The invited "old guys" drifted into and around the hooch at eight, all of them but Grady and Ken Key recon team leaders, "One-Zeros" in the local argot. The recon pecking order was unique. Regardless of rank, the new recon man was subordinate to the other two Americans in the team. It was not unusual for a captain to serve as the "One-Two" and carry a radio or machine gun in a team led by a sergeant, the "One-Zero," who had as his deputy another sergeant, his "One-One." In due course the One-Two moved up to become the One-One in his team, but the only way to become a One-Zero was to be recommended for the job by his team leader for performance in the field. The field was Laos.

The men in Day's hooch that night had served in recon for years. All were sergeants who had trained others to lead recon teams. Grady, a squad leader in the Exploitation Company was welcomed back by big brothers Robbie, Joe Waldron, Mike Schaefer and Ridgerunner.

Robbie and Schaefer joined Day in sipping Irish whiskey. Grady nursed a San Miguel beer. Waldron and Ridgerunner drank Cokes. It struck Day that none of these men were heavy boozers, rather debunking the stereotype of the hard-drinking, two-fisted, profane airborne soldier. Two of them never drank, and the other three drank in moderation. That was not typical of the CCC camp, or of SOG in general. Heavy drinkers were not in short supply. The men in Day's hooch shared extraordinary skills and strong attachment to their work, but they were very different in many ways.

Day knew that Joe Waldron liked the ladies. His sexual exploits around Southeast Asia matched his considerable combat exploits in Laos, both widely known and generally admired.

Ridgerunner did not chase hookers and wasn't a boozer. His profanity was natural, fluid, constant, Olympian. He loved the action of Chinese films of war and general mayhem without understanding a single word in Chinese.

Schaefer, married to a Thai woman to whom he was faithful, drank in moderation, rarely used crude language and conducted himself in a mature assured manner generally admired by his local peers.

Robbie's physicality leaped out, but not because he flaunted it. It just was. He killed people and broke things, but what made him tick was the satisfaction he took from matching wits with a respected antagonist in the enemy's backyard. It was like giving a sprint competitor a head start and then defeating him. A few years older than the others, he had two boys in high school in Pennsylvania.

Grady was a big strong kid in his early twenties who joined the Army to have his war. His aw-shucks manner, willingness to do difficult tasks, and desire to master the tricks of the trade made him acceptable to the experienced men gathered in Day's room. Respect was earned by courage, skill, focus on the mission and absolute loyalty to comrades demonstrated in the boondocks with bad guys shooting. The old guys were pleased to join the major in welcoming Grady home.

Quiet conversation celebrated his homecoming. His reception committee consisted of the most skilled and bravest soldiers Day had encountered in a couple of wars. His impression of troops and leaders in the Korean War were not good. Among the soldiers, he'd met tigers and pussycats. Of course there were good guys, there always are: Pep, the BAR man from Brooklyn; Buel, the sniper from Oklahoma; John, the rifleman from Rome, New York. But he remembered a few cowards and a hell of a lot of dumb guys. And he didn't see many good leaders in Korea. The U.S. Army in Germany in the early 1960s struck him as being all show, no go; too much attention to shiny boots, short haircuts and white rocks. He'd been favorably impressed with Special Forces in Germany and Vietnam. That's why he stayed with SF. That's why he was still a soldier, not a drone commuting daily to the Big Apple. Sometimes he accused himself of arrested development. The locker room camaraderie and being part of something bigger than self, he admitted, was very important to him. He readily acknowledged that he had allowed himself to care too much about the guys in Kontum. There was no denying his strong feelings of respect and affection. He knew that he should limit his professional interest to their capabilities and limitations. That was the wiser way, the Army way.

The day after celebrating Grady's return, Sergeant Key and Major Day were in the TOC, the tactical operations center.

"Major, you'll find this interesting," said Key.

"Wadda ya got, Ken?"

"The lieutenant was showing me photos from the last mission. He was picking a few to go with the After Action Report. He can tell ya about them."

Lieutenant Kingston, Robbie's One-One, separated two photos from a number of them spread out on a field desk.

Studying one, Major Day said, "Looks like a figure shooting at the camera."

"Yessir. Robbie was alternating bursts from his CAR-15 and taking pictures."

"In the middle of a firefight, Robbie was taking pictures?"

"He did."

"And this one. Do I make out bodies in thick brush?"

"Yes, sir. At one point he turned and knocked me down. I was at his left rear. I thought he flipped out. Then he fires a couple of bursts in the thick stuff to our rear. I don't know how he knew they were there.

Two bodies crumpled. Then he took those pictures. I have no idea how he sensed them. I don't think he heard or saw them. He just felt their presence. He does stuff like that all the time."

The three of them examined all the photos.

Key muttered, "That's Robbie."

***

Three images came to mind when Day thought of Ridgerunner. After the death of one of his Montagnards, Day was shocked at the little man's reaction. Two Americans and two Yards had jumped into triple canopy in Laos at low altitude. They wore fire jumper outfits: padded suits, masks fitted to a special helmet, and they carried a long drop line. One of the Yards fell to his death.

Day commiserated.

"Sorry about Phu."

"Fuck 'im."

"Why?"

"I told him what to do and how to do it."

***

On another occasion Day stepped out of the TOC for a breath of air and to clear his head, a mistake at midday with the sun burning down without mercy. His discomfort and fatigue must have been obvious as he stretched like a cat awakened from a nap, then slumped. A voice said,

"Hey, Tu Ta, I got a cold drink and a chunk of shade for ya."

It was Ridgerunner offering relief to the worrying CINCTOC. Day joined him, pleased by the highly unusual congeniality. They talked.

"How long you been here?"

"Bout five years in-country, bout three here in CCC."

"What keeps you?"

"I shadow-boxed seven years. For five I practiced my trade."

"When are you going home?"

"When it's over."

"It's over."

"I'll leave on the last bird out."

***

Four-star General Abrams came to CCC to pin a valor award on the chest of a brave medic who had alternated saving and protecting wounded good guys and killing healthy bad guys on a mission over the fence. Radich told Day to brief Abrams.

"Give him current ops and how we're organized. He doesn't like bullshit. Be brief, be right, be gone. If he wants more, I'll give it to him conversationally."

That's the way it was done.

Two tents were set up near the chopper pad where the DSC was presented, one for briefing, one for shade and cold drinks. Two recon One-Zeros waited in the refreshments tent, in case the general had questions. Day did his gig, was gone and waited with the recon men for his eminence.

As he entered the refreshment tent, the general saw the recon men and Day. He strode to Ridgerunner, extended his hand, and asked, "Sergeant, how long have you been here?"

Ridgerunner took the General's hand, glanced at his watch and said:

"I've been waiting for twenty fucking minutes."

All awaited thunder and lightning. Silence reigned. Abrams smiled. He had a good story for confidants over a drink in Saigon that evening. And for other evenings in the time left to him.

***

Staff Sergeant Joe Waldron, the One-Zero of RT Alaska, arrived in Asia in 1963 and was still there in 1970. He killed his first enemy in 1964 while advising some little people during a six-month classified tour in Cambodia. He gravitated to recon work because he liked being in charge. No one is more in charge than a One-Zero "over the fence" in Laos. Joe knew that it was improbable that he would bump into Saigon warriors, PX commandos, staff officers or clerks out there.

Joe was tails to Ridgerunner's heads: polite, even gracious to all.

Beneath the surface lurked a quest for perfection. Courtesy hid his obsession: he wanted clear missions and a free hand in their execution. His men understood the contract: do what Joe says; pull the dangerous missions; get free time; get a lot of money. The flip side was equally clear: don't cross Joe. He found in CCC the conditions enabling him to control his universe. He was a field marshal sergeant. He had run dozens of SOG missions from Vietnam and Thailand into Cambodia and Laos. Like the other recon men, he liked autonomy.

After a mission debriefing he would stand down his men, giving precise instructions regarding the date, time, place, and uniform for the next assembly of the team. He gave them money, asked if anyone wanted something from Saigon, smiled, thanked them for their good work, and said good-bye.

Joe's drills were as rehearsed as a Broadway chorus line's routine. They enabled him to do the near impossible: to break contact after walking into an ambush. Here is how he did it.

Joe's Americans, the One-One and One-Two, were a Native American and a Latino, small to medium sized brown men, just a tad bigger than the Yards. Joe was tall for a North Vietnamese, but he was slim and had skin color not unlike his enemy's. In dense jungle in a tense situation he could pass for an NVA soldier. He and his team were armed with the Soviet weapons carried by the enemy and wore NVA pith helmets, equipment, and uniforms.

RT Alaska looked like the enemy where the enemy was in control. The first action, if the bad guys got the drop on them, would be to challenge them. All armies screw up. No ambushers want to kill their own people. Alaska's worst-case drill, walking into an ambush, began by causing the enemy to hesitate for two seconds. If that happened, Joe figured that nine out of ten times he would come out on top. The tenth time he'd be dead.

When challenged, one of Joe's three-man point was designated to answer in Vietnamese, identifying them as a patrol of the 66th Regiment of the NVA. That response was intended to freeze the ambushers. It was also a command to the other point man to fire long bursts at the ambusher's voice from a modified enemy automatic weapon with a 100-round drum of ammunition until he ran dry, at which time the shooter withdrew to the left and to the rear as a second man in the point similarly armed took up the slack until he emptied his 100-round drum. Simultaneously, two men armed with bazooka-like B-40 rocket propelled grenades moved up on the right, fired their rockets, and withdrew to the left and rear. The automatic weapons men repeated their initial actions, but now at a greater distance from the ambush. Reiteration of the ballet took the team back another ten yards while fire on the enemy was constant. The drill was simple. It was also rehearsed constantly; his team could do it while exhausted or in shock.

Joe added a devilish touch. He controlled a man carrying a lightweight, non-standard aluminum 60mm mortar tube on a sling. Instructions from Joe to that man were: every time I stop I expect to be goosed with the mortar tube. As the men in front fired their long bursts and moved to the left and rear, each went by Joe handing him a mortar round. They put fresh drums, magazines and rockets in their weapons as Joe popped the rounds into the mortar tube braced on the ground without a base plate. The rapid reaction with automatic weapons fire and mortars was intended to shock the enemy long enough to put distance between Alaska and the ambushers. Ambushers don't expect quick reaction and heavy fire from rockets and mortars. Movement forward was always to the right, and movement to the rear was always to the left. They moved like chorus girls and fired like demons. Simple. Joe liked simple.

The master of mayhem worked out his pattern on paper and on the ground. Next, the pencil positions were matched to names, usually nine Montagnards and three U.S. Every item of equipment to be carried by each man was specified by Joe. Then, they went to the range to walk through drills at half speed, then full speed, then with live fire. Simple. Practice. Shock. His drill got Joe and his team out of an ambush in Laos without injury, because the enemy had engaged a force of unknown size. They had a lion by the tail and let it go.

***

Unlike most of the major's band of Regulars, Mike Schaefer considered himself Christmas help. He intended to have his war, because it was there, and to study law after it wound down. He joined the Army to see combat in Vietnam, joined Special Forces to serve with the best, and remained in-country because he enjoyed life on the edge.

After serving in an A-Team, he found his way to SOG, running recon missions into Cambodia and Laos from Vietnam and Thailand. His plans did not include marriage to a lovely Thai woman, the daughter of a Thai officer, but he fell in love and married her.

Among the recon men, guts and smarts were common, but Schaefer maxed out in both categories. His One-Two, a senior NCO who was himself brave and bright, described a combat action to Major Day that would have put Schaefer in the Recon Hall of Fame, if such a hall existed.

Contact with superior enemy force required Mike's RT Montana to move to a succession of delaying firefights as the team withdrew to a location permitting extraction by helicopter. The enemy took a number of casualties but was skilled and relentless in pursuit of Montana. Chuck, Schaefer's One-Two was wide-eyed as he described the action.

"Major, Mike defies description. If I didn't see it with my own eyes, I wouldn't believe what I'm telling you."

Chuck's animated body language punctuated his story.

"At one point I was putting out napalm that splashed on the back and shoulders of his shirt, as he controlled an airstrike. He was bringing bombs and nape real close as the bad guys attempted to get belly to belly with us. So help me, with fire burning on him as he talked on the radio, he suddenly drops two NVA that had gotten near us. He did everything at once while burning. He controlled the RT, directed air strikes, and personally shot two guys.

"The man's incredible. He does this stuff routinely with no fuss."

This commentary from a trooper of high intelligence, extensive field experience, and quick wit made Day smile at both the story and the storyteller. He knew (but Chuck didn't know that Day knew) that Chuck had proclaimed: CCC is to the Army what the Spike Jones Band is to music ... and Major Day is leader of the band.

The Americans of RT Montana were combat skilled, gutsy—and

different. The One-Zero chose an unusual pre-law course in Vietnam. His One-One was a qualified HALO parachutist who had jumped into Cambodia on a mission, detached from Montana. He was the youngest team member and let the others do the talking. Chuck, the One-Two, was a senior NCO with active duty and reserve time, going back to the occupation of Japan after the big war. As a civilian he had served as a police detective after a brief career with the circus. He volunteered for SOG and willingly subordinated himself to two younger men so that he could ultimately be the One-Zero of his own RT. Total focus on the mission made the different men compatible.

***

Day admired each of the men gathered to welcome Grady home. It hurt to know that Fat Albert wouldn't come back, and Day knew that he had allowed himself to become too attached to his soldiers: Fat Albert, Grady, Robbie, Joe, Ridgerunner, Mike, and Key. Death or maiming of some of them was a likely outcome of his planning and missions conducted at his direction. And he no longer shared risks with them in the field. That's what happens when promoted to Major; one joins the quill pushers, the staff, the REMFs. He had learned something fully understood only by those who had personally lived on the edge: It is simpler for the man of conscience to be the operator than it is to be responsible for the operators.

PJ: Friendship, Craft and Ethics

Budding journalist and bar fighter PJ Riley liked the Special Forces sergeants he met at Momma Bic's Bar. He was skeptical of the public affairs officers whose duty it was to brief, babysit, and control the press. Schaefer, Jerry Conway and several other SOG guys had tipped a few glasses with him at Momma Bic's or other bars, and sometimes at PJ's digs. The NCOs reciprocated because they liked PJ. He was earnest about learning what it was to be scared shitless, and he was prepared to put his ass on the line to find out. He sought their views regarding his "basic training," and that was flattering. They advised him to hitch rides around country, rub shoulders with GIs, and go on combat operations with good outfits and bad, U.S. and ARVN, Army and Marines. See it all, they advised, but they cautioned him to be careful at all times, very careful with bad U.S. units, and super careful with ARVN units. Experience in the field validated his trust in his coaches and their good advice.

PJ recognized that Saigon staffers and PAOs had jobs to do, but as a patriot he resented being treated like the enemy. Staff did not trust him. As the war dragged on, he concluded, the military became paranoid. Leadership in Washington was drawing down troops in Vietnam, conscripts didn't want to die in some shit hole, war resisters taunted authority, and the American people doubted the wisdom of a failing war that had lasted longer than WWII.

And the media mocked the military. Sure, there was bad reporting, misperception, and irresponsible kids playing journalist, but there was something worse than all that and more important. The media often pointed to a wart on the military nose and said: "See the wart!" The military said no. But everyone saw it. The military found itself defending shifting policies and a losing war badly conducted by frustrated leaders and unwilling soldiers. Many professional soldiers realized it was an unwinnable war, but among the SF types the attitude was elemental: you take the King's shilling and wear the King's coat, you do the King's bidding. Besides, they liked what they were doing. PJ respected that, and his SOG friends respected his seriousness of purpose and emerging professionalism that was much like theirs. They were immersed in their work in 1970. So was PJ.

He took their advice on how to get to the truth of the war by disbelieving government press releases, avoiding official briefings, and refusing to go on "command sponsored" tours. Everyone knew that reporters needed man-bites-dog stuff to satisfy their readers, but the PAOs unrelentingly showed them dog-bites-man copy and happy talk. Official releases had only good news to report, but something was clearly amiss if the U.S. was pulling out short of victory. Treated as an enemy, he came to think of himself as being the enemy—of officialdom. Treated as a friend by SF men, he identified with them. This sorting out of friend and foe seemed simple. It would become complicated.

Uncle Fred

Fred hated meetings called meetings, but "Let's go to lunch"; "Stop by for a cup of coffee"; or "How about a drink after work?" were OK non-meetings. Nevertheless, when Fred suggested he stop by for a cup of coffee, PJ knew he had a meeting with the boss.

They got comfortable. Fred made that easy.

"Before you went to the bush, you had pictures in your head. What surprised you in the field?"

That was exactly the question PJ had posed to himself.

"I was well-received. The troops wanted me to know what it's like to be a grunt. And they asked what was happening in the States.

"I learned that outfits are as different as individual personalities. I'm beginning to get that."

"You mean combat units?"

"Mostly, but I also saw it in support outfits. A truck company drives dangerous roads every day without external support—like gunships, gun jeeps or APCs with heavy machine guns—and morale is high. Another truck company has low morale.

"Chopper pilots are impressive. Period. Gutsy kids. Always ready to respond to calls from the field."

Fred said:

"Most of those kids should be driving hotrods around the town square in Ohio on Saturday nights. What else?"

"I had to see the flat delta wetlands of IV Corps and the Central Highlands in II and I Corps with my own eyes to appreciate how varied terrain is. In the south, they fight in boats and swamps. Up north, they climb mountains and are cold at night. Gotta see it. I thought Vietnam was jungle. Small country, big differences in the bush."

Fred was attentive. PJ talked.

Fred asked, "Can you care for yourself in the field? Troops notice that."

"Yes. You put me in the right dress. Troops checked me out. My small rucksack with energy bars, nuts, candy, an OG colored towel, a toothbrush, malaria pills—the big ones and the small ones—passed muster. So did my canteens and first aid packet. No loafers with tassels,

113

just notebook, pens and pencils. They saw I didn't need a babysitter and liked that.

"TV guys need cameras, sound, a talker, a lot of gear. I blend in. Troops forget I'm there."

Fred re-directed the non-meeting.

"Do you know how long I've been at this?"

"About a dozen wars."

Fred smiled. Professionals have their own metrics.

"Right. I've seen many new boys. You take to the craft. I want you to know I see that."

PJ was surprised and pleased.

Fred continued.

"I'm proud of what we do. We have our share of frauds, dimwits, and jerks. But most of our colleagues are truth-seekers.

"Do you know how most new boys in Vietnam break in?"

"No. I've been too busy tending my own garden."

"Good. Tend to business. But from time to time we need to step back and think about the 'all' of it.

"Journalists on this beat consist of older guys, like me; new blood, like you, educated, vetted and hired in the States. But some just bought a plane ticket to Vietnam and approached a bureau chief asking for a job, willing to do the leg work and face hazards in the field."

"...unlike fat cats who watch the war from a bar stool. And they work cheap."

"Right. Some become good at it unrestrained by ethics. The press in Vietnam has been at war with the military since '63-64. Young Turks reported the enemy winning. MACV PAOs were lying at the Five O'clock Follies. It became us versus them.

"Stressing bad news is as bad as cheerleading. The process has become far too adversarial. Truth gets lost."

"How do we turn it around, Fred? Pearl Harbor and Hitler made it easy: defeat evil. War correspondents were trusted. Just do your bit for 'our boys over there.' Korea and this one frustrate us. We don't like indeterminacy. We prefer crusades. But we never sorted out good and evil here. Now we just want out.

"We'll walk away from the dead, a countryside pock marked with bomb craters, and God knows how many missing, wounded, or screwed up people. And nothing is better."

"PJ, America prefers politics as a morality play: Good versus Evil. You're right about indeterminacy. We like the good guys versus bad guys. That's why our western films are popular. But it shouldn't be necessary to choose to be either a good American or a good journalist."

"I'm both. But the military thinks I can't be trusted."

"That cuts both ways. We don't believe the military."

PJ paused, thinking.

"It might take a generation to fix that."

"But it may get worse. TV is reporting in almost real time. Instead of sending cans of film from Saigon or Hong Kong to New York, the way we do now, someday we'll send live action directly from the battlefield. When that happens the public will know as much as decision makers, almost as fast. That puts pressure on decision makers."

"Fred, it's begun. They lie, stall, or spin a story. Pols once had information the public never knew about..."

"Right. That gave them time for considered decisions. Soon they'll respond before they think things through."

"And insiders leak. Sometimes it's pure spite, revenge, a chance to settle an old score. Sometimes God whispers to them, sometimes a disgruntled insider is a phone-call away from a journalist ready to run with it."

"PJ, it comes back to individual conscience. I make a lot of those calls now. Some day you will."

"I'm still finding my way around. You got me through the first days. All I can do is report honestly."

"Easily said. But you didn't report what you had for breakfast this morning."

"Point's made. We select what we report. We exercise our judgment."

"Aye, and there's the rub."

CHAPTER SEVEN

Mission Prep

Saigon

Colonel Pietro noodled and doodled. He always did just that, weighing the bits and pieces before coming to a consequential decision and considering the second- and third-order effects of that decision. Whether buying a car, planning a vacation, or selecting the right man for an important and unusual mission, intimates knew that he would doodle on a yellow legal pad that was soon covered with arrows, exclamation points, question marks, and lists with lines struck over or repositioned until he made his decision—upper case, with exclamation point, as in this case, MAJOR DAY!

His reckoning went something like this:

On the one hand, Lieutenant Colonel Radich, the CCC Commander, is capable, and the bulk of his command would constitute the blocking force on the trail in Laos. On the other hand, he's getting long in the tooth. And whatever the outcome in Laos, the CCC mission would continue and need a boss.

116

Major Day is capable, has great rapport with soldiers, is fit, if incapacitated—Pietro avoided ugly acronyms, like KIA, MIA, WIA—he can be replaced with less disruption of CCC than if Radich was incapacitated. Unsaid, probably decisive, Pietro held Day in high regard. This was not on his pad, but he saw his younger self in Day—so much for rational decision-making.

Not on his pad, but lurking somewhere in the ganglia of his nervous system and surfacing unannounced too often, was the two-year-old shock of taking his son's body from Vietnam to Arlington for burial. The multiple shocks—learning of death, accompanying the body, sharing the unspeakable sorrow with his wife—all of this before the powerful jolt, the finality of the graveside scene and the playing of Taps. The Arlington protocol was the military version of the sacred, perhaps the Stations of the Cross in Lent. The mourners assembled, were moved to the gravesite, waited for the body of the soldier, joined in prayer, listened to rifle volleys and Taps, and attended the reception at Fort Meyers, nearby. Done for a stranger, it got to Pietro. Done for his son he couldn't control the tears and did not try. Taps was the best and worst part of it.

He saw that his wife was stoic and brave—and crushed. She had suffered and waited for her husband during his year in Korea in 1950 to 1951 as an infantry company commander and again during his combat tours in Vietnam. They had been hazardous. His current job was relatively safe. The loss of her son was so ... unfair.

After a week with her in their Virginia home after the burial of their son, Pietro returned to Vietnam grateful that, though profoundly shaken, she was one tough lady. Always had been. That thought remained with him during the long return trip from Washington to Saigon in 1970. She'll be OK.

Long flights without immediate responsibility invited long spells of free association and rumination, a kind of timeout or self-hypnosis.

The special ops assignment in the Pentagon came to mind. It was a hell of a good job. Most officers in DC regarded a tour there as Purgatory, or something like taking castor oil because mom said it was good for you, good for your career. DC was expensive on Army pay, the traffic was as bad as New York City's, and many officers had jobs that were either uninteresting or so deep in the bureaucracy that they felt suffocated, small cogs in the Green Machine. Pietro sometimes felt guilt. He loved his work, theater was available, cultural activities abounded, and the schools for his son were very good. It came together nicely for him. He mulled over how his military experiences had prepared him for the JCS job that had gratified him, although at the moment in a cramped seat, he regretted that his ungrateful and puritanical government denied him a Martini or a sip of Scotch on the contract aircraft filled with young soldiers—like his son.

Previous tours—Trieste, Germany, Korea, and Vietnam in the 1960s—prepared him for the JCS job in DC. So had schools: the Army War College in Carlisle, the Command and General Staff College in Leavenworth, the Infantry School at Fort Benning. Much of it was redundant or unimaginative or both, but what the hell, like the Baltimore Catechism, it crossed T's and dotted I's. Southern Bavaria and the 10th Special Forces had been pure joy. Service with the gung-ho kids of the 82nd Airborne was a reminder that there were still true believers out there.

He smiled as he reflected on the fun he had. And the dopey bastards kept paying and promoting him! Army wisdom had it that more than one SF tour was career suicide, meaning no promotions beyond lieutenant colonel. Most SF officers were not regulars, meaning twenty years and out as a major or lieutenant colonel. Somehow he had beaten the rap. No accelerated promotions, the kind that went to the chosen few who commanded battalions and regiments in the divisions, but neither had he been "passed over," Army talk for not promoted. His last conventional command was his rifle company during the unpleasantness in Korea. He enjoyed it, but along the way he came to think of two distinctly different armies: the U.S. Army, Inc. and SF.

Before the war in Korea, he was part of an unusual outfit in the late 1940s that tried to keep the peace where the border between Italy and Yugoslavia was contested in the vicinity of Trieste. That duty fascinated him and contributed to what he often jokingly—but accurately—called his never-ending liberal arts education. He saw the clash and blending of Germanic, Latin and Slav cultures and used his Italian language skills. He met and married a German-Italian girl, a "displaced person" who found herself washed up on the shore of Trieste by the storm of the war ending for most in 1945. His son was born there in 1948.

He smiled again, revisiting scenes from his past that were positively affected by accidents and what he called the excretion of a Green Machine's Personnel Manglement Non-System. Brother officers lamented the irrationality of the non-system; he loved it.

Born in Greenwich Village in 1922, he grew up speaking Italian and English in a part of New York City that was very green because of an Italian need to grow and eat the very things that also served man's craving for natural beauty. St. Veronica's parochial school prepared him for Stuyvesant High School that prepared him for the City College of New York. When bombs fell on Pearl Harbor he found purpose when he joined millions of men around the world already in military service.

The shiny boots and pure thrill of jumping from perfectly good airplanes attracted him to jump school. That qualification and two years of college made him just right for an Officer Candidate School that produced "90 day wonders" of recent civilians ordained officer and gentleman by an act of congress and accident of birth date. Ever vigilant Personnel Manglement noted that Second Lieutenant Roger Pietro spoke Italian. Logic dictated assignment to the Office of Strategic Service, a collection of smart-asses doing secret tricks.

Thus did language skills, airborne training, high intelligence, and a craving for adventure conspire to pop him from an aircraft in flight over Indo-China during the war with Japan. Upon landing he did not encounter Italian speakers, but that skill begat OSS which begat Pietro's career which now begat the blocking force in Laos that Major Day would command.

Kontum

Lieutenant Colonel Radich minced no words. "Colonel Pietro wants CCC to run the show. As of right now, you are the ground force commander for the blocking mission in Laos. I'll give you the mission and parameters. Get back to me in 72 hours with your plan."

Major Day suppressed his desire to grin foolishly, adopting instead the mask of the cool professional. He said: "Yes, sir." But he wanted to jump in the air and click his jungle boot heels together. He got busy as commander, not staffnik, the actor, not the planner. His entire career pointed to this mission. He was prepared.

Three days later, the CCC Commander and staff assembled in the Conference Room, a place that stood in sharp contrast to the bunker that surrounded it and to the compound surrounding the bunker. The room was as elegant as the rest of CCC was primitive. A dozen seats faced a slightly raised stage, where Day stood next to a neat wooden podium and in front of large sliding Plexiglas panels. On the podium was the SOG symbol, a bloody death's head wearing a green beret. On the sliding panels were maps marked with symbols and numbers. Everything about the room said: This is a serious place.

After terrain analysis and weather forecast, Major Day summarized the situation.

Enemy trail-watchers would investigate and provide preliminary reports within hours of the Arc Light strike conducted by B-52 bombers from great altitude. The trail watchers were the eyes of the enemy and a little joke of Mars: half-naked nomads banging on tin cans or firing gunshots would warn their chain of command of the handiwork accomplished by bombers capable of delivering nuclear weapons anywhere on earth from miles above. Quick-reaction forces trained to destroy RTs would respond to the intelligence relayed to them, ultimately by NVA troops equipped with radios. Alerted by the terrain-altering B-52 strike and unusual helicopter activity, enemy forces would probe the intruders in squad and platoon strength to ascertain the size, activity, location, units and equipment of the American-led incursion. Company size units from the 66th and possibly the 28th Regiments could be on the scene in an estimated eight hours. If deemed necessary, the NVA could attack in regimental strength, possibly supported by tanks, in 72 hours and in battalion strength in 24 to 48 hours.

These estimates were not predictions. They were estimates of capabilities based on SOG's five years of experience in eastern Laos.

Major Day stated the mission, the second paragraph of the highly stylized five-paragraph field order.

To establish a blocking force at a coordinates AB12345678 on enemy lines of communication in Laos; destroy enemy troops and materiel by direct action and the employment of air power.

Simple. That's the what.

Next came execution, the how.

Infiltrate by air within two hours of the Arc Light. Dig in the main body, a company heavy with machine guns and recoilless anti-tank weapons, on constricted terrain. Destroy enemy forces. Prevent passage south. Four heavy RTs were configured as ambush teams, each armed with a 57mm recoilless rifle. Two would operate within 20 kilometers north of the blocking force and two at about the same distance south of the main blocking force. Their mission was to remain undetected until the enemy reacted to what was happening at the blocking force location. As the enemy re-routed traffic from his main supply route to avoid air strikes and to reinforce the attack on the blocking force, the ambush teams would find the alternate trails activated by the enemy, ambush and kill him by direct action and air strikes.

Six light recon teams would operate within roughly 10 kilometers of the blocking force. Their primary tasks were early warning to the blocking force and target acquisition for destruction of enemy forces by friendly air.

Coordinating instructions were vital.

A small team in an area dominated by the enemy survived by the wits and initiative of its commander. For the accomplishment of their normal recon missions and their very survival, both the light and heavy teams needed the freedom of action characteristic of SOG operations. However, this time the RTs were not alone in the area of operations. Unless the locations of all friendly forces were known, air strikes directed by the blocking force or another RT could kill friendlies. Those near the enemy's main supply route, the Ho Chi Minh trail, were particularly vulnerable to friendly fire.

Because the enemy was proficient in direction finding and target location, frequent or extended chatter on the radio was an invitation to detection, location and destruction. The enemy would locate the team and run it down. Part of the solution was for all Americans on the mission to memorize several reference points on the map. Recording them in any manner was prohibited. Such recording risked everyone on the ground, should the enemy get the reference points or marked maps. Friendly rapid fix on location from reference points was given as so many kilometers up, down, left, or right of the reference point indicated. If a team realized that a strike called by another American endangered friendlies, a code word would be used to say, "No. Do not fire there. I am in the target area."

Day stepped aside to allow the Launch Officer to explain the entire air scheme from the B-52 strike to insertion of forces, to fire support on the objective during the operation and for extraction.

Day paused briefly to allow response to questions directed to the Launch Officer before continuing with administration and logistics, and concluding with the commander's location and communications instructions.

Uniqueness of the operation drew questions from the CCC commander. Radish began.

"Can a CH-47 lift a bulldozer?"

"Yes, sir, a small one."

"Confirmed by the Heavy Lift Company Commander," said the Launch Officer.

"D-4 type dozers, developed for airborne use, can be delivered over the required distances. Engineers deliver and use them in Vietnam routinely."

"OK. Tell me about the commo wire."

Day produced a panel showing a schematic of the blocking position. On a hill mass dominating the road were symbols for the command bunker, with a view in three directions, and a medical bunker in a hollow next to a clearing. Down the slope facing north were two bunkers marked "57mm" for recoilless rifles. Trenches connected them to bunkers marked "ALT," for alternate positions. Oriented south was a third 57mm with a trench to an "ALT." Still further down the slope were three bunkers marked 1, 2, and 3. They were the platoon command posts of Exploitation Company. The perimeter was divided roughly into three pie slices, each assigned to a platoon.

He paused, allowing Radich time to examine and digest the detailed panel. He continued the brief-back.

"The terrain will be torn up by the B-52 strike. 'Bunker' is a little misleading. We're talking about holes in the ground with overhead cover and an aperture for sighting a weapon. We won't string the commo wire above ground. We'll bury it. I plan to connect the command bunker to the medical bunker, the platoon CPs, and to the primary and alternate 57mm bunkers. I don't know how long the commo wire will stay in, but until the enemy blows it away we can unclutter the radio nets by using land line telephones."

"How long will it take to build the bunkers?"

"Sir, I do not know. Some hours. But I can tell you my priorities."

"Go ahead."

"My priorities are: command bunker, 57mm primary and alternates, platoon CPs, trenches, fighting positions, and medical bunker. Time permitting, the dozer moves earth to form berms. Pierced Steel Planking—PSP—will be put overhead until enemy action stops work."

Radich tried to imagine the hill after heavy bombing and said, almost to himself:

"We can't know what the hill will look like after the B-52 strike."

"Affirm. Craters, downed trees, loose soil, dust. We'll put construction materials on the ground. Chain saws and C-4 can be used to cut and blast trees and limbs into bunker frames and roofs."

"That takes time."

"Yes, sir. Combat engineers have built fire support bases all over Vietnam. They recommended pallets of pre-filled sandbags to save time, shaped charges for hasty cratering, and the D-4 earthmover to push, pull, and lift earth. They recommended steel culverts that I plan to use to cover trenches. They come as pipe or half-pipe that can be used as overhead cover. The engineer volunteered to give me people to help, assuming the job was in-country. I thanked him, and told him to forget our chat."

Radich: "We could use a combat engineer platoon for just one day. But conventional U.S. forces in Laos is a no-no."

"Right. But I think air will keep the enemy off us for at least day one. Got beaucoup lift, tac air by day, and Air Force gunships loitering out of sight every night we're out there."

Radich mulled that over.

"Air Force priority is to support us. Show me the numbers on the ground."

Day pulled out another of the sliding panels, pausing to allow Radich and his staff to digest the information. The chart showed seventeen U.S. soldiers in Exploitation Company: company commander, first sergeant, three platoon leaders, and nine squad leaders. Day added three 57mm recoilless gunners—Americans. Radich nodded, assenting.

Another chart showed a command group of six: Major Day, Sergeant Key and four other sergeants.

"How come you plus five? Seems fat."

"I need three radio nets for the command group: internal command and control, air support, and a radio relay to you. I expect heavy traffic in crunch time."

"Makes sense."

"I want a clear head on the radios and replacement leaders and runners under my control when things get hot. When things go bad I want an ass-kicking NCO who has the whole picture."

"I see seventeen plus six is twenty-three. I see the doctor plus two medics for twenty-six. I see two U.S. per RT for twenty. That's forty-six. Tell me about the four times 57mm recoilless rifles."

"Each heavy ambush team has a 57 with a U.S. gunner. I love my Yards, but when it comes to aimed shots, give me an American. I need first round hits. Also, because of the back blast, I don't need language issues in a firefight. When the 57mm ammo is gone, I want the launcher destroyed. I want American gunners."

"Got it. Tell me about the Yards."

"There are a hundred and twenty-eight in the company in the blocking position. Seventy-two are in the RTs. Four are in each of the light teams for twenty-four. Twelve in each heavy team makes forty-eight. That's 200."

"Did you consider 106mm recoilless rifles for the fixed defensive

124

positions?"

"I did. They weigh 286 pounds and are over ten feet long. Too big. Too heavy. The 57 weighs forty-five pounds and is five feet long. Gunners will relocate after every shot. The back blast will attract enemy fire. If I expected targets beyond 500 meters I would have had to go with the 106. I love it, especially the sight and the spotting round. The 57 is good at less than 400 meters, but I expect to engage at much shorter ranges. The 57 will stop anything the enemy has, including the PT 76."

***

The Launch Officer stepped onto the platform, pulled out a panel. He went through distances from Kontum, Pleiku, and Dak To to the target area in Laos; aircraft types, ranges, and armament; weather at various places and altitudes; locations of known and suspected anti-aircraft weapons; refueling and rearmament. He concluded:

"Sir, what's new is scale. We gotta refuel and rearm faster than ever."

Radich said:

"We get fuel and ammo to Dak To, and people to turn around the choppers. We can handle that."

"Roger, sir. Here's the plan."

This chart showed delivery schedules for fuel, ammunition and personnel augmentation to assist with the extra work at Dak To.

He got that look on his face that told briefers to stop talking while the Old Man focused on an issue and sorted it out. Old guys recognized The Look.

"All CCC people not over the fence are available to help the ammo and fuel guys."

Pause.

"We get the fuel and ammo there as late as possible, so we don't tip our hand. But we don't want to cut it too thin; unpredictable weather can cause delays."

Pause.

"I'm concerned about local security around Dak To."

Day stepped back to the podium as the Launch Officer took his seat.

"Yes, sir. So am I. An attack on Dak To that blows up the fuel or ammo gums up our scheme. We addressed that in two ways. The camp commander agreed to keep two of his companies out on local patrol for the duration of the operation, and CCN will keep four RTs on the ground overwatching approaches to the camp. When I told the camp commander that he would have air support on call day and night until the end of the mission, he was pleased to cooperate. He usually operates on a shoestring. He'll coordinate his people and the CCN teams. They'll concentrate on known infiltration routes and east-west avenues of approach near Dak To."

"Go on."

"Colonel, the only thing I haven't covered is mission termination. When it's time to get out, I intend to do a rendition of the mad minute. I'll fire everything available and have air assets surround us with air strikes. I wish we were within an artillery fan, but that requires a firebase in Laos, a no-go. I'll be on the last bird out."

He uttered the military mantra.

"Sir, that concludes the briefing. Do you have any questions?"

"Not now. Do it."

Isolation

The gates to the compound were closed. As the CCC men rehearsed battle drills on live fire ranges in the Kontum area, they were escorted to and from the training areas. They did not leave the compound for PT without escort. They did not chase whores. They were isolated from the outside world. The older men knew the drill from their peacetime tours with other SF Groups. Being in "isolation" for a mission was like being in jail. Security required isolation.

The final countdown before the mission was analogous to the warm up by professional athletes on game day. The game plan had been learned, and the players were in peak form. Only loosening muscles and mental preparation remained. Test firing of all weapons meant that the prep phase was coming to an end. They focused on the enemy and terrain.

Among the enemy units known to be in the objective area was the 66th Regiment of the Peoples Army of Vietnam. Veterans of the 66th PAVN had locked horns with the U.S. 1st Cavalry Division in the Ia Drang valley in 1965. Friendlies operating in the tri-border area, where Laos, Cambodia, and Vietnam met, must sooner or later deal with the 66th. Just as Kipling's Tommy recalled Fuzzy Wuzzy with respect—"for he bruk the British square"—veterans of combat with the 66th referred to the enemy as Mr. Charles. "Charlie" was a lesser foe.

The B-52 strike on the objective area would make a shambles of the terrain. Triple canopy would collapse to form mounds, almost mountains, of leaves and branches. They would be green for a day or two; then they would be brown tinder for napalm bombing. Giant trees would be uprooted. Others would be snapped at various heights leaving a grotesque moonscape of stumps several feet high and leafless trunks taller than telephone poles. Craters would dot the landscape. For about an hour, debris in the air would make breathing so difficult that the initial incoming troops would wear gas masks. Falling trees, until they settled, would be more dangerous to the people on the ground than direct enemy actions. The task force would burrow into debris and shape it to advantage. Despite massive disorder, the hill masses would remain.

Enterprising Reporter

PJ had never pressed his SF buddies for details about their work. That was exploitation of friends, a violation of his personal code regarding trust. He was interested in what they did, their insights into close combat that they chose to reveal. So it was not unusual, considering the amount of booze that flowed when the soldiers were on standdown and PJ joined them in decompressing, that war stories were told and heard. Boozy trust loosened lips to a degree that would have enraged intelligence staff officers and pissed off professional soldiers. Some young adventurers failed to make the distinction between work and play. Professionals in less violent work do the same. Shoptalk dominates playtime among people who care about their jobs. The reporter knew the work was hazardous and secret. He put his personal relationships in one box and his professional life in another.

But that neat distinction proved impossible to maintain. He exploited his friends. The bitch goddess success cloaked herself in a robe called Nobility, Truth, Objectivity or something like that.

His SOG story was his biggest, perhaps one of the biggest in Vietnam since Tet, 1968. It was precisely that reporting that refined his craft and established him as a pro. It came out of his affection for the SF men and their acceptance of him as he was passed from friendly hands to friendly hands as a kindred soul, another wild-ass chasing thrills on the edge where high adventure and death meet. Life for the adventurer in wartime Vietnam was liberating for soldiers and scribe. Indeed, an outsider might not have been able to sort the reporter out from the warriors as the young men drank, laughed, talked, cussed, and screwed, sharing their love of life, women, and danger with one another. Soon he was a part of group from House Ten, a safe house in Saigon where SOG men hung their hats while in town. Never invited to the safe house, PJ never asked where it was. He met the semi-crazies from Da Nang, Kontum, Ba Me Thout, and the Saigon headquarters as he stood-down with them in bars, his pad, and hotels around town. Strands of his life and theirs came together as he quite inadvertently stumbled onto precisely what his friends did. Conflict resulted.

On a visit to a Special Forces A-team in the central highlands, not far from where Laos, Cambodia, and Vietnam come together, PJ heard a familiar call sign on a tactical radio as he sat sipping coffee and chatting with three SF troopers in their team house in the boondocks. The radio was always on "broadcast." Reference to "Covey" rang a bell. So did a call sign. He knew it as the nickname of a CCC recon man he knew from Saigon carousing.

The radio was monitored twenty-four hours every day. To the untrained ear, its sound was garbled noise. In time, concentration filtered out noise from message. PJ had already learned to ignore noise in the background of military communications and to pick out only the essential. The Covey call sign insinuated itself into his consciousness, probably because the tension in the voices on the radio interrupted the relaxed conversation at the camp. The listeners in the team house were not addressed, but the SF men tensed as they recognized that the extraction of a SOG recon team was in progress. They listened attentively, ready to render assistance if required.

The RT came out under pressure. No one had been hurt. The running commentary of the soldiers in the team house made it clear that the SF men in a remote location near Laos admired the SOG men. They had a front row seat to scenes from the secret war over the fence. SOG support aircraft had made emergency landings on the camp's strip. On at least one occasion men on strings were landed and then climbed into the bird for the last leg of the trip home.

When the extraction was complete and the radio went quiet, talk about SOG missions went on for an hour. Some of the yarns were literally incredible. PJ learned that his pals from House Ten were heroes to men who were widely admired as heroes themselves. He resolved to study the reporting on SOG on file in the bureau in Saigon and to tap files in New York, where researchers could support his effort. There was surely a feature story there for an enterprising scribe prepared to dig into old reporting.

***

Upon his return to Saigon, PJ did his homework. He found several articles on operations not explicitly identified as SOG operations, but he was beginning to recognize the signature of the cross-border penetrations. One Pacific Stars and Stripes newspaper piece reported, "four U.S. foragers killed in tri-border area." He speculated that the reporter missed the story by accepting the Public Affairs release saying that the Americans were killed in Vietnam in the vicinity of the border camps at Dak To, Dak Pek, Polei Kleng, Plei Mrong, and Plei Jerang. PJ saw a pattern unfolding. He surmised that the soldiers were SOG recon men killed in Laos. He wondered how many American KIA "in the Central Highlands" or "in the tri-border area" were over the fence when killed. A reporter with field experience and a little luck might put this all together. The media people who hung around Saigon, gathering what passed for news from one another and the military briefers, would remain oblivious to this story within the Vietnam story—until it broke.

Research in other publications revealed fragments of the closely-held secret operations that had been reported in magazines, journals, and newspapers. A surprising number of Americans died just on the Vietnam side of the border. Or came up "missing." Equally coincidental were the number of helicopters recovered by heavy lift choppers "near the border." It was all there in bits and pieces, but no one had put the story together. Reporters failed to ask the right questions. On which side of the border did the birds crash? Where did the soldiers die?

The press clippings, his experience on the ground and the stories he had heard from special ops friends provided the context of the story. Researchers in New York filled some gaps. So did Fred. It was coming together.

Since 1964, articles had been written about SOG, but no journalist had connected the dots. Or identified SOG. The red flag for PJ was the MIA.

SF had an unusually high number of "missing in action," even for an outfit that performed hazardous work on the infiltration routes in Vietnam from the isolated SF camps. But he had learned that good infantry took pride in bringing back its dead. SF was good, but small teams operating in the enemy's backyard often literally ran for their lives in areas dominated by the enemy. The SF "missing," he speculated, might be in Laos or Cambodia, where a team of four or six men simply could not recover its dead from an enemy numbering dozens or hundreds. And teams were overrun. Sometimes, no one got out.

Another element fell into place for PJ. The SOG headquarters on Rue Louis Pasteur called itself the "Studies and Observation Group," but it was an open secret that SOG stood for Special Operations Group. Green Berets came from and went into that compound all day, every day. Nungs, the Chinese mercenaries, guarded it. Black trucks and jeeps took Green Berets from that headquarters to black aircraft on the airfield outside of Saigon. PJ had seen the black birds on airfields around Vietnam with his own eyes. He knew CCC was in Kontum, because that's where Schaefer was assigned. He also knew the SOG guys of CCS went to Buon Ma Thuot, and the CCN men were assigned to Da Nang. If SOG was such a hush-hush outfit, how come a cub reporter could see through the transparent cover after a couple of months in country? How come no one has written a definitive piece on SOG? Surely Fred knew all this. Why not a comprehensive feature—maybe a serial with four or five parts? PJ needed another non-meeting with Fred, a conversation with his SF buddies, and a purposeful trip to the boondocks.

The very fact that actions were "classified" was a red flag and an invitation to an enterprising reporter.

PJ was enterprising.

CHAPTER EIGHT

Big Story

Loose Lips

PJ entered Momma Bic's Bar, spotted some SF pals from House Ten at the far end of the bar, and joined them.

"Co, give these Saigon heroes another of whatever they're drinking."

He was ready for some serious relaxing.

The girl behind the bar, unusually responsive, said, "Will do, PJ. They number one candy ass. Number ten GIs."

She was out of character. Normally she served drinks with the sparkle and cheer of a morose troll dispensing tokens in the catacombs of the old New York City subway system. Her bonhomie, even if faked, suggested that she and one of the marks on the other side of the bar had already made arrangements for later in the evening, promising profit to the "working girl" if not pleasure.

"Howzit hangin', PJ?"

This from one of the Da Nang men, a wiry stud whose name PJ couldn't recall. Mike Schaefer had introduced them during an earlier bacchanal in Saigon. The wiry one had an excellent reputation as a recon man. PJ could testify that the man drank and screwed with more abandon than finesse. He was another guy burning the candle at both ends. Live fast, die young, and leave a good-looking corpse was the unspoken eleventh commandment. The SOG recon men didn't say those words; they lived them.

Said Da Nang trooper had a head start of at least a couple of drinks, as did his companions, also from CCN. Their bright eyes and broad grins could be explained by either rapture of the deep or what had been in the glasses being refilled, not for the first time. Probably the latter.

"Good. Been a busy little man this week reading up on SOG. I owe myself some R&R."

"Me too. But my buddies and me gotta fly out tomorrow at oh-dark hundred. Gotta cut it short and get back to CCN to get my go-to-war-stuff. Then a blackbird ride and we'll see Mike Schaefer and them weenies down at CCC."

"Tell Mike he's due for a stand-down in Sin City."

"Rog. I'll tell him."

It dawned on PJ that something unusual had just gone down.

"What are you DMZ heroes doing down in Kontum? Don't you have enough to do up north?"

"Not sure. Maybe we decided to start World War III."

"Hey, babe! Button it," an older trooper admonished. He was reminding the younger man that he was entering the realm of CLASSIFIED, all caps. His admonishment was the equivalent of the WWII "loose lips sink ships."

"Rog," said the wiry one. "Just want PJ to know when the goin' gets tough, CCC needs CCN guys to bail 'em out of shit."

A gong sounded in PJ's head. After a week researching SOG ops and a lot of thinking about them, here was a mission taking shape under his nose. But the SOG elements, according to his sources, were autonomous. Why would CCN men go from their operational area up north to CCC's area of operations in the tri-border area? Unusual. If he hadn't been doing his SOG homework for the past few days, the bar talk might have gone over his head as just so much background noise to drinking and whoring.

He felt a sudden twinge of guilt for taking candy from a baby or overhearing the pillow talk of others. It passed just as suddenly. It wasn't as though he was pumping these guys. I walked in, and they hit me in the head with it. PJ's shit detector went on high alert as his conscience took a nap.

The wiry one, uninhibited by the flowing amber liquids and the company of boon companions, provided answers to questions not posed, proving once again in vino veritas.

"A call came to House Ten just before we left. Me and a couple of other CCN teams are gonna secure the Dak To launch site while Mike and some other CCC teams tangle assholes with bad dudes. All I know is I gotta be on the Blackbird in the a.m. and in the little bird behind the bar before that."

That was enough for PJ. The story was in Kontum. Fun and games tonight, but he decided to get out on the ground to see what was going on. That's what recon men and good journalists do.

***

In the morning, the first task was to get to Kontum. There was no way to hitch a ride with his drinking buddies in their Blackbird. They might shoot off their mouths with Uncle Sam's secrets in a bar in Saigon during stand-down, but hitching a ride in a Blackbird was a no-no. Adult supervision prevented that. But getting to Kontum was not a problem. A call to the MACV Public Affairs Office would get him there for a visit to the Central Highlands, a reasonable and routine request. But he couldn't ask to visit CCC, since neither CCC nor SOG existed. However, there was a Special Forces B team in Kontum. There was also a MACV advisory team there. That's it! Ask Public Affairs to approve a permissible visit to the MACV team. Then sniff around Kontum to find out what the hell is going on. Another twinge of guilt faded before it formed. It is easier to live with a lax conscience than with a scrupulous conscience. The latter had long since gone the way of the buggy whip. Besides, Dienst ist Dienst, und Schnaps ist Schnaps. Make a clear distinction between duty and pleasure.

PJ called his office in the morning, leaving word that he was headed for Kontum to visit the MACV team. The MACV Public Affairs Officer got him his ride to Kontum. Nothing unusual here. The eager beaver reporter asked duly constituted authority for transportation to a MACV outfit. The MACV Public Affairs Officer checks the box. PJ headed north as he legitimized what he was doing by thinking: their bat, their ball, their rules.

Easy for us big-time foreign correspondents! Grab field gear, use one's wits, hit the road, Jack!

Kontum

The loadmaster opened the C-130 tailgate even before landing, played nervously with the coiled cable connecting his telephone headset to the copilot, and shouted over the engine noises to his passengers upon touch-down: "Up and out as soon as the aircraft stops! Quickly, quickly! Stay left and right of the cargo! Watch out for the cargo!"

Passengers strode smartly down the lowered ramp, left and right of the cargo that slid down rollers in the middle of the ramp. In less than a minute twenty men had gotten off, a like number had boarded, six large bundles of general cargo were sitting on the tarmac, and trucks were pulling up to the bundles. Fellow passengers had alerted PJ that the bird would barely stop, and so it was.

The sergeant driving the jeep had no trouble finding the only civilian debarking, the one without a weapon.

"Mr. Riley, I'm from the MACV team. I'll take you to the Senior Advisor, Kontum Province. But first you can wash off the red dust and get a cool drink."

During the short drive to the MACV compound, his driver referred to CCC as "those prima donnas." He said the Special Forces B team was "OK," but later PJ learned that the SF guys called the MACV men "maggots," a silly wordplay on MACV. Only a handful of Americans in Kontum, and they're three gaggles engaged in a pissing contest. How American. PJ speculated about competition being an American disease, maybe a fatal disease.

Later that night before turning out the light, he summed up his impressions with cryptic notes to himself:

Kontum MACV team demoralized. Poor bastards depend on unreliable ARVN support in boonies. Are on their own. No creature comforts. Decreasing support of all kinds: air, log, intel. ARVN leaves advisors in lurch. Untrustworthy. Sense IT'S OVER. Counting days. Gotta get out before shit hits fan. Fear NVA will cut country in half from tri-border to Sea in vicinity of Qui Nhon. Fear enemy tanks. CONTRAST TO SF AND SOG. MACV JEALOUS OF SF GOOD SPT, ESP SOG. Some SF men returning to RVN are being assigned to MACV teams. Pissed. Rats to sinking ships. Some volunteered to return to SF in RVN go to MACV. Had positive talk with the SF B team commander. He will take me to his A-team camps, including Dak To. B-team doesn't know or won't talk about SOG. MACV dislike SOG and SF. What's going on? How can B-team not know? Don't they talk to each other?"

***

PJ re-read and edited his scribbled notes. He was on to something and determined to get the story and get it right. Research and readiness to go where the story is helps. It also helps—he smiled, recalling one of Mike Schaefer's admonitions—if you take your head out of your ass, you just might ask the right questions.

The next day, PJ learned that the lack of coordination among the Americans in Kontum and their mutual mistrust worked to his advantage. The three-ring circus of alleged military professionals allowed him to play ringmaster, to his advantage.

Dak To

Dak To was one of the four Special Forces A-team camps subordinate to the B team in Kontum. After short visits to the border camps at Dak Pek, Plei Djerang, and Polei Kleng, where all was calm and quiet, PJ was struck by the feverish activity he saw as his chopper approached Dak To.

Compared to the other camps, this was big time, more like the forward operating bases of the divisions or an artillery base camp. The lightly constructed buildings, concertina wire, punji stakes, water tower, perimeter positions, bunkers, Montagnards armed with World War II vintage weapons, and red soil were about the same as at the other camps. But at Dak To the number of gun ships, slicks, C-123s, and heavy lift choppers were more characteristic of an American conventional task force than the usual nickel-and-dime operations conducted by SF and lightly armed indigenous people. He observed several big, black rubber fuel bladders, piles of ammo, abundant engineer gear—sandbags, PSP (pierced steel planking), bulldozers—and more than enough antennas and commo vehicles to support an entire division's communications. It was Saigon at rush hour or dinner-time at a depression-period boarding house.

Absorbing the scene, he realized that just a few weeks earlier he would not have fully appreciated the significance of the sight below. Now it was crystal clear: this was highly unusual.

This was man bites dog.

At precisely that moment, the Special Forces B team commander sitting beside him gave voice to his cool professional estimate of the situation.

"Holy shit! What in the hell is going on here? What is all this? It looks like D Day!"

That confirmed PJ's take on the scene. The B team commander had not been informed of this special ops caper. He was confused, disbelieving, and very angry.

The chopper touched down in a swirl of red dust, a precursor of the swirl of recriminations that followed.

It started with the loud CCC Sergeant Major accosting the people exiting the helicopter. The old soldier was prepared, in the name of security, to chase off the bird and its passengers who were not a part of the operation now underway. They had no business here. They had no need to know.

Next came the volcanic eruption from the SF B team commander who pointed out that Dak To was one of HIS sites, that any activity here should have been cleared with HIM, that HE would take up this matter with HIS A team commander.

He inquired politely:

"Who is the fucking cretin in charge?"

In due course the CCC Commander arrived on the scene to present himself to the apoplectic major as the cretin-in-charge. His self-introduction was accompanied by vigorous finger pointing—some would call it chest stabbing—that came very close to being assault on a junior officer with a dangerous weapon. Radich, getting a grip on himself, made a cogent point and raised two questions in his own collegial manner.

"This is a secret mission and none of your fucking business."

Then, indicating PJ, he raised his questions:

"Who IS this civilian, and WHAT in God's name is he doing in the middle of my SECRET operation?"

The CCC commander, upon learning that PJ was a reporter, informed him that he—PJ—had seen nothing at Dak To. He suggested that PJ had never been to Dak To.

PJ, agitated at finding himself the scapegoat for the military screw-up, said that he had every intention of fully and accurately reporting what he saw before him. Not only that, the young scribe asserted, he also intended to draw the logical conclusions and to speculate on their significance—in writing—as soon as he got back to Saigon. Radich's invocations of "classified" and "secret" were to PJ what the moving red cape is to the bull.

"That's Laos," he said pointing west, "and I see a steady stream of traffic flying in that direction. I will not pretend that I don't! And let me remind you I'm playing by your rules. MACV approved of my visit to the Central Highlands. I am escorted. I arrived by chopper. Authorized!"

Radich turned from the reporter to his comrades. The soldiers began to sort out their differences. The A team captain told his boss, the B team major, that a classified message from the 5th Special Forces Group Commander directed the A team to give CCC all support in this important mission and to tell no one, repeat, no one, about it. That was clear enough. The B team commander could huff and puff until he turned purple, but his subordinate A team commander had responded correctly to duly constituted military authority, the 5th Special Forces Group Commander. Skipping links in the chain of command was highly irregular, but not unheard of in "black" ops. In any event, the Group Commander had spoken. That was not the fault of the A team commander whose usual concern was the enemy, not several U.S. field grade officers biting on his ass.

The CCC Commander, now in a conciliatory mode, confided that in the B team commander's position he, too, would be mightily pissed. The major, upon seeing the message from the Group Commander to the A team commander, agreed to get out of the way for the duration of the mission. He remembered that when he signed up for SF he was told there would be days like this.

That resolved, Radich turned the full force of his charm on PJ, who was as unimpressed by the saccharine approach as he had been to the earlier bullying.

"Look, Mr. Riley, I'm responsible for this classified mission. I'd appreciate a little cooperation, a little discretion."

"Colonel, two minutes ago you tried bullying me. I'm not one of your troops. Now you're trying to con me. I'm not buying that either. My visit was sanctioned by Saigon. I played by your rules. If the U.S. military doesn't have its act in order, that's not my problem."

"OK, you've got me by the short hairs. The U.S. Army brought you here. We screwed up. You shouldn't be here. I appeal to you as an American. Don't print the story. Our troops are at risk."

PJ wasn't quite sure of himself, but he was ready to deal.

"Colonel, I got a deal for you. Brief me chapter and verse on this operation—the whole deal from A to Z, including maps—the whole deal—and I'll wait until it's over before I run the story."

Radich didn't hesitate.

"I can't do that. Listen, it isn't that I won't do it. I can't. I can't brief you on a classified mission."

"I'm giving you a fair deal. I'm here legally. The PAO in Saigon approved the visit. I flew here in a military aircraft with military escort. I intend to report precisely what I saw and draw the logical conclusions. If you can't bend, I'll simply tell what I know. I assure you the story will be an honest account of what I saw here."

Radich ground his teeth and turned his back on PJ. Denied interviews with the troops, the reporter boarded the chopper and departed with the B team commander for the return trip to Kontum.

Turning from the red dust kicked up by the departing bird, Radich sincerely lamented that shooting traitors had gone out of style. It wasn't right that a kid could blackmail the Army like that. And get away with it. The old soldier immediately got to a radio to inform Colonel Pietro that the cat was out of the bag. He asked Pietro to try to kill the story in PJ's bureau in Saigon—if he couldn't kill the reporter. It wasn't like this in Korea or in World War II, he mused. The tail is wagging the dog.

Pietro and Fred

Pietro very carefully thought through his approach to PJ's bureau chief. Killing the story was out of the question. But he believed that Fred, a WWII veteran, was the right sort. If my Army is too stupid to guard its secrets, we can't expect a journalist to kill a hot story like this one. In our system, the Army keeps secrets, and the press tells secrets. That is a fact of life in our democracy. The best outcome Pietro could expect was delay of the story until all U.S. troops were out of Laos and back in Vietnam. Could Fred sit on the story for a few days? Would he?

Pietro realized that he did not know the nuances of the relationships between the bureau chief in-country, editors in New York, and reporters in the field, but he did know that he had to act quickly. He called to arrange a chat in Fred's office.

They met, each cordial, each sensitive to the professional dictates of the other. Fred said he would not endanger Americans by prematurely exposing the operation in Laos, but he cautioned Pietro that it was not the call of the bureau chief. The reporter would press to get his story printed. If the editors in New York thought it was news, timely, and the reporter got it right, they would probably run it. Fred said he would recommend that the paper wait a day or two, but the editors would go with their best judgment. He looked Pietro in the eye as he told him that the whole story would be told; the issue was when, not if.

Fred went on to tell Pietro that PJ had been working on a feature story absolutely aside from the most recent revelations. That feature would appear as a series in the coming weeks and would expose SOG's operations in Laos and Cambodia from 1964, when the CIA gave the mission to the Department of Defense, to the present. Fred reminded Pietro that SOG's cross border operations had been treated with kid gloves by the press for a long time. Now that U.S. forces were leaving Vietnam, it was time to tell the story. That would please neither the White House nor the military, but Fred emphasized the fact that PJ had researched the story using openly published sources, not classified information. This latest incursion into Laos coincided with PJ's research for the feature story. The U.S. Government had lied repeatedly about those clandestine operations, but its fingerprints were all over them.

On the other hand, it was a story of brave Americans doing the near-impossible. The Army would be smart to come clean, to put the best face on it. In conclusion, Fred repeated that he would do what he could to delay PJ's story until Americans were out of harm's way.

Ever the supreme realist, Pietro shook hands with Fred and thanked him for thinking about troops who at the very moment had their butts hanging out. He didn't say it to Fred, but Pietro had often speculated that SOG's work could not be hidden much longer. Too many people knew; too many lies, it was over. The current mission over the fence, the blocking force, was probably SOG's swan song. So be it. But it wasn't for us to blow the story. PJ, Fred and the New York Times have their mission. I have mine.

Pietro thought of American soldiers with their asses hanging out in Laos. At the personal and professional levels they were his soldiers, his responsibility, his friends.

PJ and Fred

Shortly after Pietro's visit to the bureau, PJ returned to Saigon and banged out a draft of his story. He gave his copy to Fred, allowing him time to read and digest it before they met for a cup of coffee—not a meeting.

"How was your trip?"

"Fred, it was the best yet! I did some research last week, and then this trip followed like the damned thing was scripted. Don't you think this is one of the big stories of this war?"

Fred saw a very excited young man. He knew the feeling. The closest thing to it was a fever, or maybe the feeling of anticipation as foreplay becomes orgasm.

"What do you want to do with this copy?"

PJ looked at his mentor with disbelief written on his face.

"I don't understand. I wrote it to see it in print. It's true; it's a big story. It hangs together with the planned feature on SOG. This is what we're about."

"I thought you and I saw eye to eye on what we're about. I'm about responsible journalism."

"And...? And I'm not?"

"It's irresponsible, PJ. It risks Americans by telling the story as U.S. troops are out there fighting for their lives."

"American troops are in Laos, Fred, in Laos as their commanders vow that U.S. forces are not in Laos or Cambodia. They've been running in and out of neutral countries since 1964. That is in clear violation of the 1962 Geneva Accords. They've been dishonest with us and with the American public. Aren't we about checking the use of power by government—especially illegal use of power?"

"We are. But do we have the right to risk American lives? Remember, when you tell your story you are telling it to the enemy. We should wait until our troops are out of there."

"I put that to the commander on the ground. I said I'd sit on it until it's over, if he gave me the whole story. He wouldn't. I have no commitment to him ..."

"But what about the SOG soldiers in Laos with their lives on the line?"

"The colonel made that call."

"Wrong. He is sworn 'to obey the orders of the President and the officers appointed over him.' He's running a secret mission, what they call a "black operation." His troops are vulnerable. You ask him to tell the secret. Don't you see? He can't make a deal with you. And we have no right to run the story as long as Americans are at risk. Isn't that clear?"

"No, it's not. The Army says its hand isn't in the cookie jar. We catch them in the cookies—because of their stupidity, not any cheating on my part. Now you tell me I can't say, 'see the liars in the cookies.' No. It isn't clear to me. This is what they've been doing for years. And denying it."

They were both emotional. Fred did the mature man thing.

"PJ, let's get a night's sleep and go over this in the morning."

"OK, Fred," said PJ, regretting the clash. They both felt a strain new to their relationship, a suspicion that they had reached a parting. Worse. They knew they had.

CHAPTER NINE

Execution

First Things First

The task of the beefed-up recon teams was to get in position to conduct raids and ambushes on trails feeding into the main trail that was the enemy's source of men and materiel heading south. The blocking position would set up where Fat Albert found that place where there was no bypass. The idea was simple: block the trail and destroy enemy logistics. That was the curtain raiser. On Major Day's command, the recon teams would then ambush and destroy enemy traffic wherever stopped and backed up by the blocking force. Getting in undetected was the first challenge.

Robbie

Robbie came off the strings in sparse jungle. Then Jimmy. Then Kingston. Robbie pointed in the direction he wanted Kingston to take the team. As Kingston passed, Robbie gave him an azimuth. By pre-arrangement, Jimmy remained with the One-Zero as the two of them trailed the team, deliberately doing only a fair job of camouflaging their back trail. Then they stopped and waited. Robbie's eyes met Jimmy's as each heard the movement. Robbie nodded at the M-3 submachine gun in Jimmy's hands, and Jimmy responded by taking up a firing position. The M-3 "grease gun" is an ugly duckling, but it was just right for Robbie's immediate purposes. Cheap stamped metal, it was durable. But what warmed his homicidal heart was the low muzzle velocity, a characteristic that allowed the grease gun's sound to be suppressed, almost silenced, so that the loudest thing about it was the metallic slapping of the bolt, announcing, to the target that he was about to die. The .45 caliber slug charmed Robbie. The big bullet knocked a man down.

A short burst into his chest and abdomen brought almost instant death to the trail watcher. That was the price of studying the tracks on the ground instead of the thick brush concealing Jimmy some ten feet from him. Robbie nodded his satisfaction to Jimmy, but the two men remained motionless for five minutes. They heard nothing to suggest the presence of more enemy troops, but they looped around the dead man ever so slowly to confirm that he was alone. Then they returned to the body and dragged it from the trail into thick jungle. They covered it and the trail with debris. Robbie took apart the dead man's U.S. M1 rifle and tossed the small parts left and right into the bush as he and Jimmy returned to the team.

Now at the head of his team, he led it to what showed on the map as an intermittent stream, a blue line alternating long and short dashes. The team walked on wet stones or ankle-deep in water for an hour before the leader made a 90-degree change in direction. The Montagnards carefully concealed the back-trail with debris. Robbie moved the team well into a thicket. He intended to hide there until the enemy was backed up on the main trail and had to use secondary trails. When the enemy did that, Robbie would find and kill him.

Joe

Joe Waldron led RT Alaska from the hovering birds into a hole in the triple canopy without incident. He used a small animal trail to make speed and get some distance from the insertion point. Human beings had not recently used the trail, but Joe was a thorough man. Making no effort to conceal tracks, he planted a Claymore with trip wire where the trail descended sharply while turning to the right. Keeping one's balance was a challenge. Joe thought it would take a skilled woodsman or an acrobat to detect the mine while maintaining balance and following Alaska's tracks. From that point he continued for fifteen minutes, circled the wagons for security, and waited. He heard the explosion of the Claymore about an hour after emplacing it.

Taking two Montagnards with him, he left the team in place with his One-One. Since there was no wind and he had set the Claymore himself, the only question in his mind was whether he had surprised a two- or a four-legged animal. Moving very slowly in an arc through the jungle back to the sound of the explosion, he avoided retracing his steps the way a lapsed Catholic avoids the Stations of the Cross. He paused to study the results of his handiwork while the Yards provided security. The '98 Mauser next to the bloody heap of black and green rags stuffed with still bleeding flesh gave him two answers. A trail watcher, not a wild animal, had tripped the wire to the mine. An NVA soldier would carry a weapon from the Soviet family of weapons, not the old German rifle found in every corner of the world. Confirming that the recent custodian of that worn weapon was, indeed, a solo performer—and dead—Joe took the rifle.

He then made extraordinary efforts to conceal his trail.

The team paused fifteen minutes before dark to eat cold wet rice in a thicket before moving a hundred meters, just as it got dark. They formed a tight circle, facing outward behind the Claymore mines surrounding them. Joe would decide in the morning if the team would remain safely in place or move to another location to rest and wait. It would be a day or two before the NVA had a serious problem on or near the blocked main trail. The team was in a ready position and a ready state of mind.

Mike and Montana

Well to the south of the blocking force, erstwhile law student Mike Schaefer moved Montana, a heavy team now with the addition of the 57 mm recoilless rifle, into a hide position. He conducted the infiltration the way he had learned to prepare briefs: carefully. Infiltration was uneventful—just the way Mike liked it. His hide position was an estimated half-day hump from the junction of the main trail and a secondary trail. Montana intended to cool it, to deal death when the time came. For now the form was to lay doggo and invisible until the right moment for the big shoot-out. It was unlikely that anyone would stumble upon his team in this patch of woods leading nowhere. Mike was confident that he would initiate the action. He liked it that way.

Ridgerunner

Ridgerunner had spent not one moment of his thirty-two years thinking about law or pondering truth, beauty or justice. He did spend a lot of time thinking about how to stay alive while making widows and orphans waiting in North Vietnam. Days before infiltration, he reviewed his options.

Jumping into triple canopy at night wearing wire mesh masks and padded firefighter clothing was extremely hazardous. The last time he did that he lost a man. The poor bastard had fallen to his death from a very tall tree. Ridgerunner was unsympathetic, but there must be a better way.

Following a Commando Vault, a 10,000-pound bomb that blew an LZ in the jungle, was another option. It had many of the disadvantages following a B-52 strike: giant falling trees, lots of dust and debris requiring the use of the cumbersome gas mask that was very uncomfortable and limited vision, and a certain visit by the enemy attracted to the big boom.

Daylight landing in a clearing big enough for a chopper almost anywhere in Laos risked observation, early pursuit, and ground fire during the final approach of the helicopter.

Popping into a small opening in the jungle from a rope attached to a helicopter was the best of a sorry lot of choices. But even that method could attract trail watchers to the distinctive pop-pop-pop sound of the chopper. Both sides had become expert in the tricks of the other in their private war.

Why not take advantage of the new circumstances, the noise and confusion of putting in lots of teams in lots of locations? Ridgerunner brought his idea to the Mad Major, now his task force commander.

"They say we have lots of tac air," said he without preliminary small talk.

"That's a fact," said Day.

"I got an idea I want to try."

"Go."

Ridgerunner pulled a map from a pocket. Pointing to a tiny clearing west of the main trail and half way between the blocking force and the heavy teams to the north, the little recon man said:

"I want to go in there if Covey confirms it can take a single bird. See this larger clearing toward the trail?"

"Yes."

"See the ridge between filled with thick shit?"

Day knew he meant dense jungle.

"Yes."

"There's about four klicks between them."

"I'm with you."

"I want a napalm strike on the big clearing, strafing runs, and a false insert with another bird. At the same time as the false insert on the big LZ, I want to go in on the little one. I want to come in from the west after a big loop out of Dak To."

The major had the assets.

"You got it."

"I want to go in after the teams in the north, after the company goes in, and before the heavy teams in the south."

"OK. The sequence doesn't affect the big plan. I like the deception: the napalm, false insert, the direction of final approach, going in amidst the confusion. You're due for a clean insert."

By SOG standards, Ridgerunner's use of air assets was profligate, but Major Day had them and intended to use them. He figured that America had lots of fuel and bullets and very few Ridgerunners.

Ridgerunner left. He said, "Rog." Soft G.

It was done. The unusual activity in the remote area and the pyrotechnics apparently masked the tree-top approach. Or it was good luck. Or the trail watchers were napping. Or Buddha or Mars wanted it that way. The little sergeant didn't ask why. The team got in free and lost itself in Laos. Fact.

The Blocking Force

Covey observed and reported to all who could hear him that the Arc Light had exposed the trail by blasting away the jungle's roof. This was the center ring for the circus that had come to town. Giant trees were piled in dangerously random patterns, reminding him of Pick Up Sticks, a game Carpenter had played with his little sister when he was a boy. The trick was to pick up a stick without moving the others. In this game, falling big tree could be as lethal as an enemy gunshot or grenade. The teams were in without incident. Some false insertions in the wake of the B-52 strikes in the north and south effectively masked the actual insertions. So far, so good, but Covey never forgot that his friends were in the enemy backyard.

The lead platoon of the blocking force, en route or hovering as the big bombs fell on the objective, was inserted under the further cover of pre-planned tactical air strikes around the hill mass where Fat Albert had conducted his recon while his team hid. Napalm ignited the vegetation blown about by the B-52s, and soon a ring of dirty smoke concealed the hill from the surrounding jungle. As the troops organized themselves on the debris-laden hill, they moved slowly. Day had insisted that the men in the blocking force wear flak jackets and steel helmets. The troops, accustomed to light battle dress, didn't like that and cursed the Mad Major as they sweated under the additional weight. But wiser heads among them saw the point. If they were to stand and fight from this position for several days, the NVA would come at them with everything they had. Bunkers, steel helmets, and protective vests would remind some old-timers of Korea and lives saved there by protective gear. The younger guys buttoned their lips when the senior citizens explained that body protection replaced mobility as life insurance in prepared static positions.

Gas masks protected them from inhaling the abundant dust and smoke lingering well after the B-52 strike. The awkward masks limited vision, which in turn made all movement awkward, which in turn contributed to discomfort as sweat streamed down faces and into eyes. Whirling chopper blades blew dust on soggy bodies reminding the troops that light infantry is a friend of discomfort, pain, and fatigue. A famous American football coach had it right: fatigue makes cowards of us all. Grime added discomfort to fatigue and anxiety.

Pre-mission drills in Kontum had anticipated the conditions encountered. Several RTs had done bomb damage assessments—BDAs in recon-speak—of previous Arc Lights. The squads fanned out to secure the landing zone that would be their umbilical cord to Dak To, America, and mother. Demolitions teams expanded the LZ by blowing down trees and tall stumps that endangered helicopter landings, and the platoon leader reported a two-helicopter landing zone in a saddle between the top of the hill and a smaller hill. That was the LZ initially used and improved. It had been selected by map recon, confirmed by Covey, and improved by the initial elements of the blocking force.

Further down the hill, however, Covey spotted a three-helicopter LZ with an approach permitting the birds to hug the treetops as they arrived and departed. That had not been picked up by map recon or by a pre-mission over flight. Removing canopy revealed the true contour of the earth, much the way a stripper reveals her essence by ridding herself of bubbles, fans, and veils. Day noted this gift from the Lord, who sometimes giveth and sometimes taketh away. Gott mit uns, thought Day—this time.

While intense aircraft activity was new to the NVA in this part of the world, the operation involving so many people and aircraft was also new to CCC and SOG. The abundant tactical air support stunned the enemy and gave the Americans feelings they called warm fuzzies.

The Major was monitoring fragmentary reports of a successful insertion when the platoon leader on the ground reported:

"Covey, relay to Circus 6: one U.S. KIA, two little people WIA, one serious."

"Shit," thought Day, in-bound with the main body. "What now? No way I figured effective enemy action so soon after the big bombs.

150

Even if NVA troops survived, how the hell could they function? Should be stumbling around like a guy beat over the head with a two-by-four."

He resisted the temptation to clutter up the airwaves with psychobabble posing as command responsibility. Too many commanders demanded reports before the tactical leaders in contact with the enemy had answers, while the guy in contact was still sorting things out. He remembered too well too often trying to field questions from higher headquarters before he was sure just what the hell was going on around him. He did not join the ranks of the "squad leaders in the sky," higher commanders who got in the way of the working stiffs on the ground. In a few minutes he'd be on the ground. Shut up. Let the platoon leader get his act together before grilling him.

Chopper blades agitated dust as the platoon leader directed the bird with the command group to land on downed branches and leaves. Half-blinded and gritty-eyed Major Day, Sergeant Key and four sergeants with radios unassed the bird to stumble through forest debris. Boxes of grenades and ammo for M-16s and M-60s were dumped from the bird. A dead American and a Montagnard bleeding through bandages on his arms, legs, and trunk, were lifted aboard the chopper. Nose slightly depressed, the bird flew close to the ground, gathering speed before falling off the hill and climbing away.

The platoon leader guided the command group to a depression serving as the command post. Resisting the temptation to ask how the casualties had been hit, Day said:

"Report."

"Sir, I got three squads at the base of the hill in all-around security. No contact. Right here is the place I recommend for your CP for now. We have two LZs. One is good for three birds the other for two. Next we build up and dig in."

He could wait no longer.

"No contact, three casualties. What happened?"

The platoon leader looked him in the eye:

"No excuse, sir. Stupid shit. Nichols was fooling with the B-40 he carried, dancing and jumping around. It went off almost at his feet and killed him. One Yard in his squad was scratched, and you saw the other one. It wasn't booze or drugs, sir. I checked it out. He wasn't high. He was just raring to go. Good judgment wasn't his strong point. He just did a dumb kid thing. And died for it. I'm pissed and sad."

Day put an arm around the platoon leader. He did more touching in Vietnam than in what passed for civilized society. Mixing young wild men, explosives, and dangerous machines, he thought for a millisecond, means somebody will be hurt. Folks back home—and even rear echelon commandos—have no idea how many "combat" injuries are accidents caused by kids motivated more by heart and mood than brain. Prudence didn't put any of us out here with the bad guys and bugs. Self-preservation said stay in college, drink beer, chase girls. We attract the other kind, the wild men.

The millisecond passed. He turned back to the here and now on a hilltop.

"Don't try to figure it. Pissed and sad is right. Look after your people. Continue the mission. The command group will handle the build-up. You give us all-around security."

Before allowing the platoon leader to move off, Day indicated the left and right limits of the platoons, once they were in position. He would feed the arriving troops into the expanding perimeter using his command group. The platoon leader on the ground had guides waiting to take them to the sectors prescribed.

***

The build-up defied Murphy's Law by going as planned, except that a kid who should have been in college somewhere blew himself up and injured two comrades while playing guns. The uninterrupted flow of birds into two LZs allowed organization of the defense at a faster rate than anticipated. The process was further accelerated by the use of big CH-47s capable of carrying an entire platoon of American-led little people and the Air Force version of the HU-1, the November model that could carry more troops than the Army version. Day got his people in position quickly.

A perimeter for all-around defense was established with machine guns set up for interlocking fire close to the base of the hill. Grazing fire, streams of bullets paralleling the ground and very close to it, was the intention. One of the lessons re-learned early in the Vietnam War—in every war—was that firing low increased the likelihood of producing casualties, even when the primary target was missed. Ricochets and rocks also inflict wounds. Rookies fired high; experienced infantry fired low. Properly positioned interlocking automatic weapons provided a deadly wall of steel as a final protective line.

The 57mm rifles were placed for maximum effectiveness a little higher on the hill so that gunners could see out to the edge of the clearing created by the air strikes. Because the back blast of the 57s would reveal their location after the first shot, each had an alternate firing position. They would shoot and scoot, but they wouldn't shoot until so directed by the blocking force commander. Day saw them as his little surprise for the NVA at the decisive moment. Initial use of airpower would allow him to hide his organic firepower and to shock assaulting troops later. If the weather turned bad, the 57s would provide some compensation for lack of tactical air, especially against tanks or personnel carriers.

During insertion the Air Force responded quickly to calls for tac air. Napalm dropped on the far edges of the B-52 strike killed or injured trail watchers arriving on the scene and discouraged others. Burning foliage created dense smoke that concealed friendly activities. The burned out area also extended fields of fire, to the advantage of the defender.

NVA commanders knew that something big was happening on this critical point of their main supply route, but lack of lowest level tactical intelligence denied them a clear picture of American activity. Massive aerial activity was alarming. Big bombers followed by tactical aircraft and the sound of troop-carrying aircraft behind the smoke exceeded anything experienced in that part of the world by friend or foe. The NVA had to think far beyond the dangerous but accustomed task of running down small recon teams. Today was very different.

At least company-size assaults would be necessary to eject the Americans. Perhaps more than that would be required. But no commander wants to exhaust his soldiers by running them up a hill and down again. Counter marches are tiring and frustrating. They also suggest to soldiers that their commanders don't know what they are doing. The best troops available had to be used to crush the Americans, who landed in strength and were obviously building combat power behind the smoke.

Where to act first was the question.

Aggressive patrolling must bring back information to be processed and fitted into an intelligence picture. So far only one trail watcher had relayed information that reached the NVA commander, and it wasn't very helpful: "many enemy" had been brought by "many aircraft" after the "big bombs destroyed jungle." That merely confirmed what one could learn by listening with his own ears. NVA commanders regretted the delay that allowed the enemy to consolidate, but they had no alternative. Before committing troops to react, they wanted a clear picture of enemy activity and what it meant. The Americans might be pouring divisions into Laos.

Grady on OP One

As the small bulldozers and troops with hand tools were transforming the patch of jungle hilltop into a strong point, the first enemy troops were observed. A two-man outpost of the platoon oriented north saw movement in the tree line.

The OP was well concealed in deadfall and had cleared lines of sight through the brush to their front. One of the observers, Sergeant Grady, looked at the enemy some 200 meters away through his binoculars. He saw the face, pith helmet, tan-green shoulders, and AK-47 of a soldier facing him in a prone position. The man gave a hand signal, presumably to troops behind him. Some five meters from the enemy soldier was another man whose tan-green hip and leg could be seen through the glasses. He detected two more unidentifiable sources of movement, but he saw no other human forms.

The American pressed the push-to-talk button of his radio twice to break the rushing sound of the monitoring radio at the platoon command post, a prearranged signal that meant "enemy in sight."

"Go, unknown station."

"OP 1. Estimated squad NVA 200 meters from my location on azimuth 05 degrees. They are a few meters into wood line from burned up area."

"I say back. From your location on 05 at 200 meters estimated November Victor Alpha squad in wood line. Over."

One break in the squelch meant "Roger," yes, correct, affirmative. The method obviated the need for speech from friendlies close to the enemy.

"Rog. Keep them under observation until you hear final approach of tac air. Then lay low. Then report."

Break in the squelch.

The platoon leader relayed the mission to FAC. FAC talked to a pair of A-1 birds in orbit out of sight or hearing from the blocking position. They were "dedicated birds," aircraft whose reason for being was to support the blocking force. They were on station. To avoid spooking the target, FAC remained out of sight and hearing until his service was requested. He also delayed firing his marking rounds until the last moment before the arrival of the attacking aircraft. FAC put the marking rounds on target. "Shit," reflected the American with the binoculars, "I've worked these babies at 50 meters from bad guys in thick bush. 200 meters in the open with FAC right up there marking is a piece of cake."

Grady saw two bombs fall from the first bird and two more from the second. Then he saw the two enemy soldiers and the jungle around them simply vanish in four successive explosions. The radio came to life. It was FAC.

"OP 1, howzat?

"On the money. Repeat. Then put 20mm on the rear, to the north of that location. Might get some departing the area or arriving."

OP 1 asked the platoon leader if he should go forward to assess damage. The platoon leader responded.

"Negative. Maintain hide position. Be advised friendlies will be to your front in approximately one five minutes. Observe from present location. We will confirm their return this location to you. Get cozy. Figure how you get back to me by night and by day."

Both men at OP 1 watched the friendly patrol appear and disappear as it slowly moved past the OP to the area just bombed. The patrol checked the results of the strike as Sergeant Grady told his Montagnard to get some sleep. It promised to be a long and lonely night.

The patrol returned as it was getting dark. OP 1 was notified that there were no longer friendlies to their front.

"Oh," thought Grady. "I'm CINCWORLD, Commander in Chief of the World."

Major Day: The Main Body

The patrol reported to Day. It had seen five enemy dead and body parts scattered about like debris after a beach party on a windy day after the fire had gone out. It brought back seven enemy weapons and a dazed and wounded NVA soldier. The prisoner said that there had been nine of them. He believed that only he had survived the air strike. He also confirmed that his organization was the 66th NVA Regiment. His battalion headquarters was located in a rest area some five kilometers to the north. Soldiers from another infantry regiment were also in the area. He didn't know their numerical designation. A VC battalion was also in the area picking up supplies to backpack into Vietnam. Near his battalion's command post was a truck turn-around point. The major noted the mention of the 66th. He had tangled with them before and knew that he was up against the best. The enemy troopers would be thoroughly pissed to have their rest and recuperation spoiled by the biggest operation the Americans had ever conducted on the trail.

***

The blocking position was beginning to look like the schematic Day had shown his commander in the CCC conference room briefing. Since the small bulldozers delivered by CH-47s were so useful in getting the bunkers and fighting positions ready quickly, he brought in four. Two would be flown out at the end of the second day, and two would stay to finish the job, to be destroyed in place, if necessary. They did the work of hundreds of men digging with entrenching tools or D-handle shovels.

Getting his troops underground before the NVA commander could estimate the situation and act was Day's first priority. The initial phase of the battle would go to the winner of the contest between the diggers of holes and the seekers of intelligence. In real time that meant that almost all construction would have to be done on day one.

It was. The groundhogs completed their first task before the enemy's scouts completed theirs. Assessing the state of his hasty fortifications, he admired the efficiency and energy of his men. He speculated that Americans do precisely this kind of work better than any other people: work that married human energy and technical competence, but perhaps most particularly, work that really needed to be done. During the Korean War, then-PFC Day saw caves capable of hiding a battalion. The enemy built them the hard way, with pick and shovel. Those caves were monuments to enemy determination and discipline. The Vietcong and NVA demonstrated similar determination and discipline in the ant-like activity in constructing incredible tunnel systems, some of them literally under their enemy for years. Motivation was the source of their strength. The Prussians of Indo-China drove French colonists from Asia and seemed prepared to drive the Americans from Vietnam.

But no one else could have done what had been accomplished on the blocking position in just hours. American ingenuity and great wealth made that possible. American technology collided with Vietnamese discipline and the willingness of their leaders to make extraordinary demands on their people in a test of will. Day regarded his SOG troops and the NVA soldiers facing him as the best. The talent and energy in the immediate neighborhood was about to be tested by the best representatives of two very different cultures.

He caught himself and smiled at his inclination to ruminate far and wide even while he wrestled with a pressing matter of life and death. Thoughts of films, sports and theater: "High Noon," "The OK Corral," show time, curtain time, and kick-off time flitted through his mind. Gentlemen, start your engines.

"Hell, there's more than one way to relax," he said aloud to himself.

Sergeant Key also smiled at the Mad Major talking to himself. Key didn't find that unpleasant. The offbeat behavior of his boss pleased him. Key was convinced that there were enough standard dipshits and puffed-up frauds. The Army needs oddballs to lighten the mood, especially when bad things were about to happen and promised to get worse. Key had his pet theories. One of them was that the badder it gits, the gigglier a trooper should be. Like when it's so wet that even the last square centimeter of a man's private parts is wet, the only thing to do is sing and laugh. He and Major Day were giggly, saw that in each other and liked it a lot.

At Day's insistence the command bunker was down the slope, well off the skyline. U.S. units built bunkers that stuck out like the Empire State Building on the top of a hill in Vietnam just as they had in Korea twenty years earlier, probably because commanders wanted to see 360 degrees from one point. But the top of a hill was just too good a target. His command post—CP in GI-talk—covered with pierced steel planking—PSP in Army-talk—and tons of earth had two long and slim horizontal apertures allowing almost 250 degrees of visibility. A manned OP on the opposite side of the hill, and also well down the hill, covered the blind spot, thus providing all-around observation. It also served as an alternate CP.

That, he thought, is proper use of the military crest. Recruits learn in basic training not to bunch up or skyline; field manuals tell us not to put bunkers on the hillcrest; yet in Vietnam, as in Korea, bunkers sat on hilltops, on the skylines. He wondered why his Army didn't practice what it preached. Why the distance between aspiration and what we do? That's because church homilies have more to do with aspiration than behavior. That defines Virtue and Sin by proximity to aspiration. Hmmm. Back to business.

***

The 57mm recoilless rifles were now in bunkers above the machine guns with line-of-sight to where the tree line met the torn-up area. Access to alternate firing positions was via trenches with overhead cover. Little bulldozers had covered the culverts with soil disturbed by bombs; roots and stones were blasted with demolitions. Bunkers for the machine guns and fighting positions for the riflemen further down the slope were all well camouflaged with deadfall that littered the landscape. Nightfall found Day's troops in the ground with overhead cover, grousing again about the need to wear helmets and flack jackets. Bulldozers, shaped charges, PSP, steel culverts, and pre-filled sandbags on pallets delivered by the CH-47s had transformed the torn earth and fallen foliage into a mole's version of Paradise.

Anticipating probing and a possible night attack, the commander established outposts and listening posts for early warning. Their mission: observe, report, direct fires, and stay alive. Select the safest route back to the main body and use it to avoid decisive combat with the enemy. It was not their mission to do and die.

Back in Kontum he had emphasized this point by telling the troops that he was tempted to arm men on LP and OP with pistols to stress the idea that they were not to take on the bad guys, except in self-defense. Their job was to direct the fire of others. But, since the CAR-15 or M-16 was useful in directing gun ships at night with streams of tracer rounds acting as pointers to the enemy, the men on OPs and LPs carried automatic weapons. In truth, he didn't have the heart to put troops into no-man's land armed only with pistols.

The proper response to a ground assault was to bring maximum firepower to bear on the enemy. The NVA learned early in the war that the best way to avoid death from the sky, or from the best artillery in the world, was to get so close to the Americans that they were unable to use air or artillery for fear of killing friendlies. NVA light infantry consistently demonstrated great skill, courage, and discipline in neutralizing enemy advantage by getting belly-to-belly with the Americans. The key to sustaining the blocking position was to hold the enemy off while punishing him from the air.

In his counterpart's place, Day speculated, I'd go for it tonight. He doesn't know how well dug in we are. He wants us outta here before we prepare defensive positions. Surprise! I'm dug in. You got the numbers; I got position and the firepower. You want it? Come and get it.

OP One

Grady heard movement to his right front, at an estimated thirty to fifty meters. He tapped his push-to-talk button twice to break the squelch, nudged his Yard companion from dreamland, and wondered why he had an urgent need to piss just as World War III was about to begin.

"OP 1, you hear enemy."

The platoon leader had one station on his radio net. OP 1 was the only show in town. His response was a way to say 'I love you,' or 'You ain't alone.' Or something.

OP 1 responded by breaking the squelch once for "affirmative." No voice transmission.

"You can't speak; enemy is close."

One break.

"Rog. When you can talk, come up."

One break.

Grady listened as enemy, maybe five or so, passed from his right front, to his right rear. He decided that remaining in place was for now better than moving. The sound of crunching dead foliage that betrayed enemy movement would betray his. NVA troops passed his hide position on the left. His reactions: loud little bastards; the loud little bastards are now behind me. He heard two distinct groups. There might be more. He assumed they were enemy recon patrols. Good assumption. Small teams were advancing to probe the American defensive positions.

He started at the sudden outbreak of automatic weapons fire to his rear. Chill in his guts became ice. It warmed as he realized that he wasn't the target. He relaxed to give it a think.

The purpose of the probe was to discover the location of defensive positions, particularly heavy crew-served weapons like machine guns or mortars. Defenders returned fire with individual weapons: M-16s, CAR-15s, and the 40mm grenade launcher, the weapon the troops called "the thumper" for the distinctive hollow thump it made when fired. He admired the gutsy enemy soldiers crawling to 50 to 100 meters from the blocking position. The defenders fired illumination rounds with the mortars. Smart. Save illumination from the air for later. Don't let 'em know that we own the whole air force. Friendlies in bunkers and trenches were engaging enemy troops in the open. The U.S. mortar positions were not easily detected in a saddle on the reverse slope of the hill. Day was waiting for a more lucrative target before revealing just how much air support he had and how responsive it was. Meanwhile the defenders popped illumination rounds from mortars. The rounds splashing around Grady were friendly fire.

Grady reacted correctly to the illumination provided by flares swinging lazily and playing shadow games from slowly descending parachutes: he shut one eye and put a hand over it to preserve night vision in one eye. No amount of training could have kept that eye closed in the minutes that followed.

To his immediate front, no more than 200 meters distant, he saw movement as dozens of figures dropped to the ground and then froze. Numbnuts, he thought. Better to freeze standing than to move. Behind them were dozens more. The illumination had caught the NVA emerging from the woodline. They were coming from a trail near where the Skyraiders had dropped their bombs earlier. Dumb, thought Grady. Then he realized that the enemy probably didn't know exactly where that action had taken place until they got there. It was likely that there were no survivors from the first engagement to warn their comrades. And they didn't know about OP 1.

In the few seconds that seemed a long time, the young American estimated what was happening. The enemy main body was following close behind the probe of the American position with an assault by a couple of companies. There had to be an assembly area in the woods behind the enemy skirmishers, and right now NVA soldiers were being guided and organized to overrun the Americans. The attackers would never again be as vulnerable as they were right now! Whoo-ee! Troops in the open! Git 'em!

Using the battle noises to mask his voice, he got to the floor of the OP and talked to his platoon leader on the radio.

"High Wire 1, OP 1."

"Go."

"I got a hundred enemy troops in the open to my front and more behind them in an assembly area. Where the Skyraider did his main act today. Gimme Spooky. I direct. Keep illum going so our target doesn't move. Out."

***

Early in the Vietnam War, some clever rascal decided that an aircraft with long loiter time capable of carrying a heavy load was needed to interdict at night. Some birds designed as cargo carriers were transformed to gun ships: C-47s, C-119s, and C-123s did the job, but the AC-130E, call sign Spectre, evolved and became the star of the show. With modifications, the C-130 trash-hauler became a killer-bird. It carried four 20mm multi-barrel cannons and four 7.62 caliber machine guns. Capable of speeds over 350 knots, it was also able to slow to below 150 knots, a capability that earned the affection of troops in contact with the enemy at night. Making lazy turns, Spectre could keep a steady stream of fire on its target. In addition to guns, the AC-130E carried a powerful searchlight and sensors, including forward-looking infrared target acquisition and direct-view image intensification sights. Since it was capable of flying over 5000 miles with a maximum payload, that meant it could fly an orbit over Vietnam all night long. Infantry loved Spectre by night as much as they loved Skyraider by day. Both birds carried a lot of deadly stuff. Both remained on station for a long time. Both could fly low and slow and hit targets on the ground.

When OP 1 called, a dedicated bird was just out of sight at 10,000 feet waiting for the call. It was nice to have friends in high places.

The lieutenant on the hill spoke.

"OP 1, Spectre three minutes out. Approach is from your right. Use this freq. He's yours."

Grady had never used this bird in anger, but he had used it in training and had once seen its awful effects after an enemy night attack on Dak To. All he had to do was steer the bird to the target area by voice and mark the target. The pilot did the rest.

Grady also knew that marking the target was his death certificate.

"High Wire, Spectre."

"This is High Wire. Talk to OP 1. Go, OP 1."

"Spectre, this is OP 1. I have you in sight. Turn left a tiny tad and you will overfly the target."

"Rog, turning tiny tad left. What do you have?"

"Estimated 300 troops in the open."

"Kee-rist! You made my day! How mark?"

"Long burst of tracer to center of mass. Distance 200 meters from me."

Spectre response was immediate.

"You call, we haul. Do it."

"Short countdown: 3, 2, 1."

On "1," Grady aimed at what he estimated to be the middle of the enemy formation. He had slipped an all-tracer magazine into his CAR-15 as he pushed the Yard to the bottom of the hole. CCC men routinely carried one all-tracer magazine to mark targets precisely like this one.

The aircrew saw the tracers clearly pointing at the enemy and moved the magical sights to begin 100 meters from the source of the tracers. The pilot intended to saturate the ground along the line of tracers from 100 to 300 meters. Once on the target the infrared sight focused on the images that were enemy soldiers. There they were! Hundreds of them! He pressed the trigger for the four 20mm guns, depressing it for about three seconds. Then he fired his four Mini guns for three seconds. He alternated bursts between the systems to allow barrels to cool. Fire was constant.

The sound was a series of cacophonous burps and belches. The sight, however, was striking in more than one way. A beautiful multicolored cascade from the sky became a splash as hundreds of tracers ricocheted in every direction, describing a flower arrangement above and around those dying in terror.

From OP 1, on the edge of the cascade, the beauty of the sight and the sound of the burps were accompanied by other sounds. The swishing of the projectiles in air was heard a millisecond before the sound of rain splashing, and that was just before the shrill screams.

In the impact area sight and sound blended to produce terror, confusion and shock. Sometimes pain accompanied death. Sometimes death made its rounds alone. But death always won. The targets were mystified by the accuracy of the very first rounds and numbed in their helplessness. There was literally no place to go to escape the killing beam that became many lights as it hit the earth.

Grady knew he was a dead man. He held his left hand against his left ear and the radio handset tight against his right ear as he squeezed the push-to-talk button.

"High Wire 1, you take it! Fire for effect! It's tearing them up! Enemy will be on me in a flash."

"Roger. Got it. You gonna move or hide?"

"Move. No way they missed my tracers. Probably got something coming my way now. Gotta git outta this place."

"We stopped illum. You got the dark. Drive on."

"All the way. Out."

Grady waited for the last parachute flares to hit the ground and burn out before he led his Montagnard partner out of their position.

As soon as the NVA recovered from the shock of being hit, even before they heard the aircraft, the OP took ineffective fire from two sides. Bursts of AK fire swished over them. In minutes the enemy or his grenades would be in the hole. Its location was fixed in their minds by the long burst of tracers fired to mark them as the target. Grady decided it was better to chance infiltrating through the troops who had conducted the probe than to wait in the hole for retribution. General confusion was his best friend.

The enemy in the killing zone was no immediate threat to the pair of friendlies in no man's land; the enemy somewhere between them and the blocking position was.

It was impossible to move quietly in the dry brush, but battle noises partially masked the sounds of movement. In lulls between bursts of fire from the sky and shrieks from the wounded, rustling was heard from both the direction of the enemy main body and from the direction of the blocking force. Enemy troops moved out of the killing zone toward the OP, and some of the probing force was moving away from the blocking position, also toward the OP. The sergeant and his companion stopped to listen to the intermittent sounds around them. Then they crawled toward the blocking position along the route of withdrawal selected earlier. After some minutes of cautious movement in no-man's land, the pair came face to face with three enemy soldiers.

They almost bumped heads. The American and the Montagnard reacted first, and three NVA troops fell to short bursts from the two CAR-15s on full automatic.

At ten feet, thought Grady, there was no missing.

The CAR-15 bursts were followed by flashes from AK-47s. The last thing Grady and the Montagnard saw were the flashes from the right and from the left front. As the rounds found the bodies of the two of them, the young sergeant observed that there was no pain, that he had run into an enemy squad on line, that the stars were out, that he could pee now, that at ten feet it was true: there was no missing.

He thought of the gold medallion and chain around his neck. An NVA officer pulled his pistol from his holster and fired twice at a range of one inch, first into the head of the American, then into the mouth of the Montagnard.

The Main Body

Major Day looked at his watch: 2245. Half an hour had passed since the OP reported the target, directed an air strike, and probably met its end out there in the darkness. He instructed Spectre to continue working over the original target and enemy routes of withdrawal or reinforcement to the north. Covey would move the AC-130 to altitude before using bombers. The pair of loitering Skyraiders would use high explosive bombs and napalm in the area between the blocking position and where Spectre had torn up the enemy attack. The probers would now die. Spectre would return to work the assumed assembly area and the enemy's probable route of withdrawal, once the A-1s had expended their bombs. The exhausted, shocked men, many of them wounded, would find no relief from American pressure. The C-130 orbited on call, out of sight, always there, like a guardian angel.

The Major directed the first platoon leader to get his troops hunkered down to avoid injuries from stray bombs and to prepare a squad size patrol. As soon as the A-1s departed, after bombing no man's land, the patrol was to move to the gun ship's killing zone. Its mission was to maintain control of the battlefield and assess battle damage.

The American squad leader, old enough to order a beer in his home state but not much older, briefed his eight Montagnards deliberately. Their English consisted of little more than a dozen basic military commands, such as: wait, come, and follow me. Confident that after much repetition the soldiers understood the mission, he led them through the wire into the dark unknown. Following a strip of white engineer tape through the friendly mines, he picked out a star behind his objective and moved toward it. His men followed in single file. Just like Halloween, he mused in a free association of memories and feelings he used to fend off fear. He wondered how others handled fear.

It took an hour to move to the killing zone. The squad leader didn't know it, but he was near the spot where OP 1 had first observed the partially concealed NVA soldiers. To his immediate front was the first of the many cadavers he would see—and smell—in the next eight hours. He also smelled cordite, still smoldering fire, and something else burning. He didn't speculate about the something else.

In accordance with the scheme briefed to his people, he found a depression from where he could monitor activity to his front. Monitor. Can't see shit. I guess that means listen. And imagine. Without a word, two-man security teams moved about ten meters to his left, right and rear so that he could concentrate on the action ahead without fear of surprise. Charlie, his best English speaker, and a second Yard remained with the American. A glance at his watch confirmed the time. About five hours until first light, when he would be joined by another squad. He had gone over the mission like a nun rehearsing her students' catechism: No sleepy. We look. We listen. Shoot only if attacked. Security all directions. Sergeant talk radio. Aircraft shoots. We no shoot. OK?

The sergeant, who aspired to admission to a good university one day, thought that he'd have to do something about his rhetorical skills. Me student, you dean wouldn't cut it at Princeton.

Focusing on the invisible area to his front, a kind of murmur was audible. When that registered he imagined the pain of his wounded enemies, sprawled where they had been deposited by Spectre, the bombs, and the mortars. From time to time he heard sharper shrieks and cries from men unable to endure the pain. Then he heard what he understood to be healthy men come to carry away the NVA dead and wounded. He didn't feel heroic as he pressed the push-to-talk button on his radio.

"Spectre, this is One Papa."

"Rog, One Papa."

"I got enemy troops in the open."

Sweet Dreams

Before rolling up in a poncho liner, Day advised his leaders to rest and trust deputies so that leaders would be alert for the serious killing ahead. He told Covey that he expected two kinds of enemy activity in the coming 24 hours. First, truck traffic will back up under the green canopy along the trail, on turn-around points, and on alternate trails. Second, enemy troop formations will make a beeline to the blocking position to overrun it. All recon teams were to be given a situation report in the morning. He wanted to notify them that events were moving faster than anticipated. Exercising caution, recon teams will move in the morning to likely target areas. The next day promised to be busy.

After passing a brief SITREP to the CCC Commander at Dak To, Major Day told Sergeant Key to mind their store for two hours.

As he dozed off he allowed himself just a bit of self-congratulation. His troops were dug in. The first round had gone to the guys in the white hats. The NVA commander had taken heavy losses and was probably scrambling to get overwhelming force to the blocking position, worrying about very effective and abundant American air power, and concerned that he had a tiger by the tail.

His next-to-last thought widened his smile: Bet the poor SOB is getting a lot of help from his bosses. The interruption in re-supply to the south was certain to be a major irritant to NVA leadership. All the way from General Giap to the commander of the 66th NVA Regiment the word would be out to destroy the Americans quickly. Hanoi smelled victory in the south. The barrier on the trail had to be brushed aside swiftly.

His eyes were heavy with sleep as he thought of his wife and their seven-year old son. His final thought before he slept was of two more good guys dead. Grady knew he was a goner when he put the tracers on the enemy, but he did it. Not for the first time the major wondered how his rich and spoiled society produced men who willingly gave their lives for their friends. Most of them came from God's Little Acre or big city slums. And the Yards. Just a few years from running around the boonies bare-assed naked, they fought loyally with American leaders. And died for them. I put those good guys out there. Rotten deal, he mused drowsily. Then he heard Spooky firing again where he caught those troops in the open in front of OP 1. The patrol from the First Platoon has something. Maybe movement.

Good soldiers. Ours. Theirs. He slept.

CHAPTER TEN

Ridgerunner Wins the Lottery

Pietro: Do No Harm

Pietro's body was in SOG headquarters in Saigon as the operation to block the trail began. But his head was in Laos. He reminded himself that grown-ups of his choosing were conducting business and doing so professionally. Three notions found themselves on his yellow pad.

Once he issued the order, men would die. He and his smartasses conceived the scheme, higher headquarters approved, and now his troops were in the second day of executing it. He re-learned a lesson from his past experiences in combat: it was morally harder to give the order from a comfortable office than it was to do the job at the cutting edge. Guilt was a part of command responsibility.

Second, it was difficult to shut up and get out of the way of the operators. Pick the right people. Monitor events. Assist when called upon. Don't be a pain in the ass. Mark was often a pest that way, as were too many senior American leaders. The commander on the ground was dealing with confusion and noise requiring some time to sort things out, to make order out of chaos. He was busier than the one-armed paper-hanger as he considered enemy activity, put his people in position, controlled air assets bringing in troops and providing air support, all the while hearing the whisper in his ear saying, don't screw up. He didn't need some high-ranking squad leader in the sky to bug him with questions he couldn't answer until he figured out just what was happening. The situation looked simpler from a chopper above the tree tops than it did from the ground with limited visibility, lots of noise and vines holding one back. Controlling troops and fire support was paramount. He did not need some HQ twit yammering on his radio. So, Pietro said to himself, shut up. Do no harm.

Third, he had the press on his mind. Shit. I tried. Focus on the mission. What the New York Times says about the operation is above my pay grade. Let PAO and the boys upstairs, the generals and admirals in MACV, Hawaii and Washington deal with press fall out. Worry about how you help your guys in the shit in Laos. Watch. Do not meddle.

Day and the Main Body

The operation punished the NVA. But an American squad leader was seriously wounded, and two Montagnards were killed as they policed the battlefield near the blocking force. The enemy was scrupulous in attempting to deny the Americans knowledge of how badly he had been hurt, but this time the carnage could not be concealed.

Sunrise revealed a jungle red with blood. Body pieces littered the area. Clothing and raw flesh hung in trees, and a solid blood trail disappeared into the jungle to the north. Following that trail, contact was made, resulting in the friendly casualties and two more dead NVA soldiers. Bodies had been dragged away. It was evident that a large force, probably a battalion, had been mauled.

Again the A-1s bombed along the blood trail leading north. Before noon the first platoon was carrying stacks of documents, friendly KIAs and WIAs, seventy enemy weapons, and three NVA wounded. The grisly task of counting enemy dead caused more than one man to vomit. Repeated passes by Spectre and fighter bombers had literally disintegrated and atomized human forms, rendering them unrecognizable bits and pieces of meat, some raw, some cooked. An estimate of one hundred killed seemed about right to the people doing the counting.

"Count the legs and divide by two," said a squad leader.

"Count peckers and you don't need no math," said another.

Crude and mordant GI humor maintained the semblance of sanity, avoiding or postponing surrender to despair at the grisly sight and stench, the stuff of future nightmares. Later interrogation of the wounded POWs revealed that an estimated one hundred and thirty died. Another estimated two hundred were wounded. The wounded NVA soldiers were not to be envied by the dead. Infection, painful death or physical mutilation was likely, given the austere medical support available to the enemy. A senior NVA sergeant was captured only because he had been rendered unconscious by blasts. The veteran of fighting the Japanese, French and Americans since 1943 said it was the worst experience of his military career. He had been under attack from the air before, but this time death had rained from the sky without warning. He was one of hundreds of NVA who were advancing with local VC guides under the concealment of darkness, when bodies were ripped apart as though by divine intervention.

Even in shock the veteran soldier retained self-control, refusing to answer any questions of tactical intelligence value to the Americans. He was a hard case. The contrast between the old pro and the young enemy soldiers impressed Major Day. He had observed enemy who behaved as comrades to their captors within minutes of capture. The moment of capture was tense. Anything could happen: a movement misunderstood; a trigger pulled in response to actual or imagined danger; a murderer, theirs or ours. But medical attention, a smoke, a smile, warm food, and POWs visibly relaxed as it dawned on them that they might be out of the shit. The transition from expectation of death or torture to a sense of safety worked a small miracle as enemies of a few minutes ago uncovered a shared humanity.

Combat soldiers shared the here-and-now immediacy of battle with the enemy, a feeling not shared with their own armies in Saigon or Hanoi or Washington. That something was certainly not shared with civilians snug abed. Hate propaganda was a ploy civilians and rear echelon commandos used to dehumanize the foe. Combat soldiers saw the enemy as their mirror image, despite pretend tough guy jargon that made them Japs, Krauts, Gooks, or Slopes. Fear mingled with respect for the foe. It wasn't very sophisticated, but unreserved contempt was saved for REMFS and politicians.

Pleased with tactical success, Day took no pleasure in the human suffering he held at arm's length by something called professionalism.

Younger POWs, probably sullen and resentful conscripts unconstrained by professionalism, revealed in an almost conversational manner that a regimental headquarters was nine kilometers north and about one kilometer west of the trail. A field hospital was also in that vicinity, secured by NVA soldiers of their regiment and some local VC. About seven kilometers north of the bombed area was a large turn-around point for trucks. According to the now-chatty POWs, smoking American cigarettes and enjoying C-rations and good rice, drivers from the north went as far south as the turn-around point where they rested before driving wounded troops back north. Others drove the vehicles to the south, through this very place where the Americans now blocked the route. The turn-around point was filling with vehicles delayed in their efforts to continue south. Day digested the information. He decided to exploit the situation.

Ridgerunner Moves

Ridgerunner was closest to the target identified by the POWs. Day talked to Covey. Covey talked to Ridgerunner, who moved toward the target.

He moved his team on a small-game trail running in the general direction he wanted to go. Then he took to the thick bush where the going was considerably slower but safer. Bentson, the One-One, was a laconic hillbilly. He played a sweet guitar, sang well, and, like his leader, had an animal extrasensory communion with the jungle. Their Montagnards were fortunate to have two Americans as at home in the bush as the Yards. Since Bentson was small and black, like them, the

Yards called him "Sergeant Yard."

Bringing up the rear, he heard it first. He patted the butt of the Yard in front of him and held the palm of his hand toward the man. Stop! The Yard repeated the pat and the signal to his front. So did Ridgerunner. Three men looked to Bentson. He tugged his ear, inclining his head. All listened. There it was! A murmur. He moved his hands as though guiding a steering wheel. Ridgerunner and one of the Yards nodded a "yes" as Ridgerunner pointed toward the sound. Bentson and the Yard who had heard the sound nodded. Ridgerunner signaled, pushing his extended palm downward from chest to waist several times. The pace would now be that of a snail. He set one foot down, stopped, and listened. The others mimicked his "Alabama high step," a technique assiduously practiced in that sunny clime to avoid stepping in mule shit. That was the way the four of them moved toward the sounds of traffic for the next hour. With every step, the noise was increasingly identifiable as trucks slowing and coming to a stop. Surely the enemy had security elements on the avenues of approach to the turn-around point, but the RT had not been detected—yet. That was the pay-off for staying off trails, maintaining strict noise discipline, and avoiding mule dung.

Ridgerunner faced the recon leader's classic dilemma: get closer to the target in order to observe better and report more accurately—with the attendant risk of being detected by the enemy—or estimate the distance and nature of the target while remaining undetected. And alive. A more reflective man, a Mike Schaefer, would wrestle with the problem, turn it over and over, weigh the advantages and disadvantages, and come to a conclusion that could be justified in a court of law. A sound method.

That wasn't Ridgerunner's style. "If I don't see it, I can't report it right. Gotta be factual, even if ya gotta hang it all out." He decided to rest his very own eyeballs on whatever was making the motor noises.

Slow high stepping continued until he saw the main trail. The underbrush was so dense that he was almost on the trail before he saw it. Stop-and-go sounds told him that he was close to truck parks and turn-around points. The canopy made observation of the trail from the air impossible. He noticed that some of the smaller branches up high had been tied to one another with vines, thus forming a tunnel through the jungle. He admired the handiwork of the men he was about to kill.

A parade of raw facts marched double-time through his head.

"Lucky to get so close without detection. Tough to put observed iron on the target. Tough to get outta here. Double tough to get out after we bring pee on 'em. Any visual signal from me and they're on us like stink on shit. Gotta back off and use a reference point visible from the air. That hole we came through on the insert. Yeah. From there on an azimuth to here. I guide Covey or FAC by sound to fly over me. He fires a marking round in the middle of the fuckers. I estimate that's 200-300 meters west of this spot. So I move east 100 meters now. Marking rounds will be about three zero zero from where I stop to talk to Covey. Worry about gettin' out later. Probably their security troops will be lookin' for an RT putting distance from target. Mess up their heads by hunkerin' down in some thick shit right around here, close to the target. Can't check every bush. Hide tracks real good. Maybe Crazy Major don't want me to execute now. Check it out."

That was, as they say in staff schools, his estimate of the situation. It was complete: friendly and enemy situation, terrain, mission, coordinating instructions, logistics, command and signal. Good junior troop leaders sat under a tree to consider all that for an hour or so. The higher they get, the longer it takes. It took him 30 seconds.

The RT took twenty minutes to backtrack 100 meters. Ridgerunner didn't literally "backtrack." He returned doing the high step on a new track parallel to the one he made earlier. No sense blowing it now that I got 'em in my sights. Put the team in a thicket, set out the Claymores, and put himself in the middle with three men in the prone facing outward before talking to Covey.

"Covey, Ridgerunner."

The recon man's guardian angel up there but out of sight answered instantly. He was making holes in the sky, ready to respond to a call from any of the CCC teams on the ground.

"Covey."

"I got a big turn-around point off the main trail. Estimate 20-50 trucks there. You read?"

"Rog."

"Relay to High Wire 6. Ask: execute now or wait? I can hide. Estimate I am inside enemy security."

"Wilco. Wait."

Day monitored this conversation from his CP at the blocking position, but he did not break in to talk directly to the RT for a couple of reasons. First, Covey, with unobstructed line of sight from the air, got Ridgerunner "5 by 5," loud and clear in commotalk. Day heard Ridgerunner garbled but readable, "3 by" in commo jargon. There was no need to rush the process and risk misunderstanding. He chose clarity over speed in transmission. Moreover, hearing the questions twice, once "3 by" and once "5 by," gave him time to think.

"High Wire 6, Covey."

"Go, Covey."

"Ridgerunner has a target: truck turn-around area with estimated 20-50 trucks. Question for High Wire 6: execute or wait? He can hide in place."

"Covey, tell Ridgerunner: do it. I say again, execute."

"This is Covey..."

"Break, break. This is Ridgerunner. Roger, High Wire 6. Wilco. Break. Break. Covey, do it."

When Covey relayed to Day, Ridgerunner heard both sides of the communication and realized that he and his commander could talk directly, without relay by Covey. Commo on tactical radios in the rough Laotian terrain was unreliable. Experience conditioned RTs to turn to Covey to talk to the rest of the world. It was good to know that at least for the moment he could talk directly to the blocking position. But displacing even a hundred meters might change that. Commo in the jungle was always an iffy proposition. Put a terrain feature between two stations and there would be no direct commo. But Covey was always there.

Ridgerunner asked, "Covey, waddaya got?"

"Babe, I got the whole world in my hands."

"You or FAC?"

"FAC does it better."

"Gimme FAC."

The Forward Air Controller, who had been monitoring, broke in.

"Ridgerunner, FAC here. Call sign, Death Dealer."

"Death Dealer, Ridgerunner. I got 20-50 trucks, supplies, troops in the open, and a headquarters."

"Ridgerunner, I got low and slow, I got fast movers, I got iron, nape, cannons."

"Rog, Death Dealer. Talk to Covey. From where he inserted me, go on 270 degrees. Listen for me. I adjust. As you go over me, I say 'Bingo.' From 'Bingo', go 300 meters on two seven zero. You mark. I confirm. Then bring in all you got. You read? Over."

"Roger. I say back. Azimuth 270 from your insert point. You give me 'Bingo.' I go 300 meters and mark. You adjust."

"Rog. If I go quiet, hammer the fuckers west, north and south of your mark. Beaucoup bad people and trucks here."

"Rog. Break. Break. Covey, you read?"

"Roger. Trail me to insert point to begin your two-seven-zero track to target."

The two birds overflew the small clearing where the RT had been inserted. Covey indicated it to Death Dealer, who crossed it on a due west track.

Ridgerunner heard the FAC approaching. As the small bird passed overhead, the pilot heard one word: "Bingo." Poised to react instantly, he fixed his eyes on a point about 300 meters ahead, aimed the bird at that point, and fired a marking round.

All the while FAC had been talking to Ridgerunner, he had also been talking on another net that Ridgerunner could not monitor, to a flight of two Skyraiders on station but out of sight. He also had a pair of F4s on strip alert in Da Nang. He would work the Skyraiders until the F4s arrived. Then he planned to use the F4s. If he got some secondary explosions, he was prepared to continue the process for as long as either he or the man on the ground believed they were doing more than grinding up the jungle. Observed targets in Laos along the trail were rare. So was the priority he enjoyed. It was his understanding from his pre-flight briefing that he, indeed, had the whole world in his hand. Secondary explosions would suggest that the American on the ground had somehow gotten into a big logistical complex. Secondaries were the barometer that told him what was under the green roof. FAC was excited. So was the usually cool Covey.

Destroying a single truck on the trail was the cause of some elation on a typical day at any Airbase Officers' Open Mess. If this guy on the ground really had 20 to 50 trucks and an NVA headquarters, this would be one of the biggest shows ever—in the south, in Laos or in Cambodia. Everyone wants to play in the Super bowl. Up north, near Hanoi, was a different story. It may not have been worth the price in men and machines, but there had been lucrative strikes up there—when political authority permitted them. Down here, destroying 20 trucks is big time.

After Death Dealer popped a marking round as he flew over the RT, he called the strike birds. Never had he been more aware that he linked the grunt on the ground to the best that the United States Air Force had to offer. He was proud of what he did for a living and proud of his competence.

"Pony Express Lead, Death Dealer."

"Pony Express Lead."

"Do you see my mark?"

"Negative. Turning. Wait one."

There was a pause.

"Got it. I was turning when you popped. Got it. Nape or iron?"

"Start with iron on the mark. Later we go to nape."

"Rog. HE on the way. Want it wide or long?"

"Wide."

"Roger, wide."

The A-1s came in side by side, each dumping four bombs. Immediately there were two small secondary explosions and a big one. Death Dealer noted that probably two trucks were blown up, contents unknown. Those small secondaries were gas tanks going boom. The big one was ammo. It could have been on a truck or on the ground. Probably on a truck, he thought. Stuff in transit probably never touched the ground. It stays on the vehicle as drivers relieve one another.

He made a pass over the target. Because he flew lower and slower than the bombers, he could see more than the busy A-1 pilots could see in an attack. In another incarnation FAC had been an attack bird jock. Strike pilots had a lot of things to keep them occupied: driving the big machines, selecting weapons systems, arming them, putting them on target, and double-checking flight and weapons instruments, all the while talking to one another and FAC, checking instruments, and looking for anti-air weapons and targets for the next pass. Careful. Don't hit good guys. Busy like one-armed paper-hanger.

The initial attack was a free ride. The NVA relied on canopy and camouflage to hide whatever was down there. On the second pass the bombers could expect every NVA soldier in the vicinity to fire his weapon at aircraft.

FAC returned to the target to see the angry green tracers climbing toward him from the ground as his eyes searched the jungle. The bomb explosions had knocked down some trees, exposing a road and a turn-off. That's what he was looking for, and that's why he used HE rather than napalm first. He wanted to see through the canopy. Napalm certainly had its uses—it covered a larger area than HE, and it cooked off ammo—but it obscured the target with flame, then greasy smoke. He planned to finish up with napalm to burn off jungle to reveal what was in the area. For now he stuck with HE.

FAC reasoned that the turn-off was for parking vehicles off the main trail. He marked it with a rocket where it turned left from the main road.

"Pony Express Lead, three secondaries. Have visual on a junction I marked. Approach it from the right at a right angle to your last pass. Use HE."

"Rog. Coming around with HE."

The twinkling of numerous tracers was a frightening danger to the aviators. But it was a deadly serious error by the ground commander. The bombers, FAC, and Covey, who was observing the entire scene silently from a higher altitude, all realized that the ground fire described a circle roughly 1500 meters in diameter. The enemy had effectively drawn a goose egg around the target. FAC immediately alerted Da Nang that he wanted another dozen sorties, maybe more. He would use whatever was sent, but he made it clear that he wanted max use of Skyraiders. Low and slow is the way to go, he repeated to himself, recognizing his foolish little-boy poetry. This was the big kill hunters dream about. FAC was entitled to a bit of foolishness after months of staring at green on green, risking his ass for non-targets.

On the second pass the attack aircraft produced a small secondary and a large one. More segments of the trail were exposed as concealment was blown down. Strips of trail took on patterns allowing all pilots to play a game of "fill in the blanks." FAC used the A-1s to pound the target area.

***

Major Day monitored the strike radio chatter from his bunker on the blocking position. Sounds good. He was elated. They had hit the jackpot. The operational objective was being achieved. Time was being bought for the Saigon government. And they weren't done.

He was also proud of Ridgerunner's skill and courage, but he was concerned that the little recon man would need his whole bag of tricks to get out of the target area alive. If we really plaster the target, he thought, Ridgerunner believed he would be safer going deeper into the target for extraction, rather than away from it. Suppression of ground fire from the air might be the salvation of his team.

But that was for later. For now the blocking force commander savored the destruction of the truck park.

He listened to the radio while reflecting on the A-1 Skyraider with affection. The old bird was perfect for doing the job for Ridgerunner. It had gone into production for the U.S. Navy in 1945 with a payload greater than the B-17 of WWII fame. The Vietnam War version was the Air Force A-1. Infantry preferred it to fast movers as much for its low stall speed as for its carrying capacity and stay time. It could fly in excess of 300 knots, cruise at 200, and slow to 120 to put bombs and cannon fire on target. The short hop from Pleiku also meant it could get to Laos fast and stay long. It was an oldie but goodie.

***

Death Dealer was also an oldie but goodie. In contrast to the popular image of a toothy young tiger, white scarf fluttering in the breeze, he was a forty-eight year old lieutenant colonel, plump as Santa Claus, whose idea of a big time was smoking his pipe, reading letters from wife and kids, looking at pictures of his grandchildren, and listening to Glen Miller tapes before turning in at 9 p.m. On his wild nights he was with Ella Fitzgerald until 10 p.m. He cut his teeth on P-51s in 1944, flew B-26s as a "policeman" in Korea in 1951, and rescued pilots coming home from downtown Hanoi in 1966. Orders on his desk said that in thirty days he would be at Wright-Patterson AFB, Dayton, Ohio, where he owned a house, his wife was a teacher, and his kids had married and settled. If promoted, in three years or so he would retire and tend roses. If not promoted, he would retire within a year to tend those roses. Nice to be a full colonel, but either way was all right with him. These sugarplums were put on hold as he entered the target area to determine where to put the next strike.

A simple "repeat" to the strike birds would allow him to remain at altitude and direct the show from a safe place. He could stay alive. He could go home. But, he was a pro. He had to do it right.

Ridgerunner had been admiring the work of professionals and enjoying the sound of secondary explosions when sight and sound compelled him to break his silence. Through a hole in the jungle he saw a cone of fire reaching for the FAC. The sound of automatic weapons came from all directions. Death Dealer was in big trouble and might not know it.

"Death Dealer, Ridgerunner. Get out! I say again, get outta there! They're on you!"

The FAC actually saw a truck and three kneeling NVA soldiers shooting at him as he fired his marking round at the truck, ignoring the warning. He then said: "Pony Express, repeat HE on my mark."

Those were his last words as either AK rounds or one of the several .51 caliber machine guns found their target. Covey saw the heavy stream of ground fire converge on the cockpit of the little FAC bird and would later report that the pilot was almost certainly hit, possibly killed, before his fuel tank exploded on impact.

Requiescat in pace, Santa.

Covey broke the silence first on his air control net.

"Break, break. Pony Express, Covey. Hit Death Dealer's marking round. I'm your FAC."

The high performance jocks were with the program.

"This is Pony Express Lead. Wilco, Covey. I saw him go in. No chute. Probable KIA. Watch your ass! Beaucoup ground fire. Target well defined. Help us work it. Over."

"Roger, Pony Express."

Again the Skyraider flight dropped high explosive 500-pound bombs, and again there were secondary explosions.

Covey sent them to higher altitudes and worked the fast movers, the F-4s from several bases in Vietnam and others from Thailand, as they arrived. They were variously armed with iron bombs, napalm and rockets. He used them all, varying directions of attack to protect the pilots from ground fire. Between strikes by the jets, Covey brought the A-1s back down and worked them. The opening of the jungle revealed more and more of the trail system that the slow-flying aircraft used to guide their 20mm strafing runs. Covey requested another FAC to work the target, since Covey's mission was to maintain airborne control of the entire AO, in support of CCC. Then he got on the command net to tell Ridgerunner, Day, Radich, and Kontum that Death Dealer was down and a probable KIA. Day took advantage of the radio contact from Covey to tell him and Ridgerunner to be thinking about extraction.

Ridgerunner counted fifty secondary explosions. The job was finished with napalm. Burning off the jungle revealed the trail, requiring the enemy to risk observation from the air or to build an alternate route. It also cooked off fuel and ammo over a broad area.

He told FAC to use the smoke to cover his extraction by strings. It was surprisingly easy. Cobra gunships put nails all around the hole used by the RT to get out. The worst part of the extraction was the leg-numbing ride to Dak To and the chill to the bone caused by evaporating sweat.

***

Two other RTs were less lucky or less skilled. One never made radio contact after insertion. Since the team had a back-up radio, Covey and Radich assumed that it was so quickly ambushed that it never reported a "Prairie Fire," the call for immediate extraction. The insertion birds neither saw nor heard what happened.

Another RT was in radio contact with Covey when it was overrun. The action took place at an indeterminate point under the green roof. No one could help. Unless Covey could pinpoint a team's location, the marvels of modern military technology were as relevant to the team in trouble as the price of hog bellies in Chicago. Three light teams were still active in the AO, walking the narrow line between death and effectiveness.

PJ, Fred and the Big Story

As CCC duked it out with the NVA in the field, Fred and PJ failed to reconcile their differences regarding the release of PJ's SOG story. It was a big story that had to be told. The issue was timing: to tell the story now, or to wait until U.S. troops were out of Laos.
On the one hand was the risk to the troops.

On the other hand, no professional journalist could fail to see that it was a big story. Fred and PJ were sitting on an exclusive, one already drafted and ready to go. Delay risked exclusivity. Media competition was keen.

Fred did the right thing. He had long ago concluded that the final arbiter in questions of right and wrong was man's conscience. If this matter were a simple ego trip, he could have crushed PJ, who was, after all, still a rookie, though a gifted one. But this was a matter of right and wrong. Fred suspected that PJ's 1960s values resonated better with the current editors in New York than did Fred's 1930s sense of propriety, personal or professional. The right thing was to send PJ's copy to the paper with Fred's recommendation that the story be held until U.S. troops were out of harm's way. That's what he did.

The editors didn't give the matter a second thought. Without hesitation, they ran it. Man bites dog. It had to be told. Soonest. As was said in Mafia circles, PJ was a "made" man.

CHAPTER ELEVEN

Robbie's Fight

The Main Body

Sergeant Key and Major Day were dining elegantly, C-rations cum plastic spoon blanco, while listening to the somewhat less-than mellifluous rushing sound of several radios in the command post. Key pontificated on the human condition, the meaning of life, the relative merits of ham and lima beans compared to beans and franks, and the nuances of delight in cocoa and cookies stacked up against a can of peaches or pears. He glanced at the major and saw that his boss had that look on his face.

"C-rats are one of life's vastly underestimated treasures and one of the reasons a man finds a home in the Army. Coffee, sir?"

"Please, Uncle Ken."

Key placed his canteen cup half-filled with water on a short green can from which he had removed the world's sweetest cookies. Since there were three cookies, he broke them in half to ensure equity, thereby preserving the combat strength and morale of the command group. The can's sides had been perforated with a little handy-dandy can opener called a P-38 to admit lots of air. The P-38 was worn on dog tags hanging from American soldiers' necks since Ernie Pyle covered World War II. As he revealed truth, beauty, and justice to those within hearing, Ken Key rolled a piece of C-4 about the size of a mothball until he had given it a polliwog tail. He lifted the cup, placed the C-4 at the bottom of the can, touched his cigarette to the tail, placed the cup on the can, and announced:

"The oven has been set for twenty-three seconds."

The putty-like explosive burned with a white and blue flame that quickly brought the water to a boil while Key tore the corners from little paper bags of sugar with his fingers and the little plastic bags of coffee and cream with his teeth.

"Save the cream and sugar, Ken. Today is Sunday. And what does CINCTOC do for his merry band on Sunday?"

"Bless you, Major, and the horse you rode in on," said Uncle Ken as his favorite boss pulled a towel-cushioned bottle of cognac from his rucksack.

It had been Day's Sunday custom in Kontum to serve the officers and NCOs of his S-2/S-3 section coffee and cognac. Sunday was a working day like any other—except for the cognac at the major's hooch. Not Scotch, not bourbon, not gin—cognac and coffee.

Key put the powdered coffee in the now-bubbling water. Day poured cognac into the metal shot-glasses that emerged from his rucksack. The little glasses telescoped into one another. They had seen frequent service on ski trips in Europe, from Germany to Austria to Italy and Switzerland.

The three commo men not sleeping or otherwise engaged joined him and Key for coffee and cognac.

"Every day in the Army is just like Sunday on the farm," said one.

"I wonder what the poor folks are doing today," said another.

They sipped.

Key broke the silence they had savored along with the belly and chest-warming glow produced by good cognac in good men.

"What's next, boss?"

Day had the feeling that Key could read his mind.

"I'm going to turn the tigers loose. Now."

He took the radio handset and transmitted the code word to set the RTs in motion.

"All stations, this is High Wire 6. Lion Tamer. I say again, Lion Tamer. Break, break. Covey, relay 'Lion Tamer' to all stations and give me Roger from each."

Day wanted all elements to get the word to execute at the same time. Experienced combat soldiers were constantly aware of how terrain affected radio communications. Day couldn't be sure that all teams would receive his code word message from him at the blocking position. Terrain would certainly find one or another RT on the wrong side of a hill or in a depression. Covey flew in high lazy circles with unobstructed lines of sight to each of the RTs until each acknowledged receipt of the message to go after the enemy. Then Covey informed Day.

***

If Day had artillery support, he would have used it to break up enemy formations invisible from his location but almost certainly setting up in the nearby jungle in preparation for an assault on the blocking force. Using expensive air assets for the purpose was a bit unusual, but given the priority of his mission and the unavailability of tube artillery, he intended to use air strikes on likely enemy targets. And that's what he did, putting bombs and napalm on the wooded approaches to his defensive position. Pairs of birds first worked over the wood lines closest to the friendlies, where unseen NVA would set up during daylight hours to observe the Americans.

His experience as a rifle squad leader in Korea, and as an infantry lieutenant platoon leader in peacetime Germany, told him that one of the toughest tasks of a junior combat leader is controlling his soldiers in the woods in a night attack. On a dark night in the woods—even in the woods of Germany, cultivated to garden-like perfection—he had found himself controlling no more than one or two of his forty soldiers, when he wasn't lost, stumbling into trees, or falling into holes. It would be infinitely more difficult for NVA leaders to maintain control of their soldiers while moving in the dense jungle under American fires from the air and from the blocking position. Anything the enemy could find to control his troops would be used—like getting through unknown terrain in daylight, marking routes, using VC guides familiar with the real estate, getting close to the objective unobserved, and pointing out dangers and intermediate objectives to subordinates during daylight hours. Surely the Major's enemy was doing that right now. And it was likely that enemy soldiers were in tight files. Dispersal in dense vegetation made control impossible. That meant the enemy was most vulnerable to American air power right now.

As the attack bombers did their job, CCC soldiers in pairs moved carefully to outposts and listening posts from which they would give early warning to the defenders in the coming battle. The idea was to make it impossible for the enemy to close with the friendlies in a rush. The NVA soldiers moving into harm's way were fully aware of the risks in facing American firepower, but they also knew that they had to get as close as possible to negate American airpower. The pressure of the enemy attack, the confusion of incoming and outgoing fire, and the air strikes would make safe re-entry of OPs to the blocking position unlikely until the battle was over. If the OPs and LPs were to survive enemy and friendly fire, they would probably need to hole up, remain undetected, and pray a lot. They knew the fate OP 1, but they also knew the terrible destruction of enemy forces that was directly attributable to OP 1. It was intelligent use of firepower versus enemy numbers and courage. But that required brave Americans watching and listening from OPs and LPs very close to the enemy.

Day wanted to patrol into the jungle to keep the enemy off balance, but daylight patrols were simply too hazardous. Repeated bombing had created an irregular band of debris around the blocking position reminiscent of a World War One no man's land. Soldiers attempting to move from the hill to the jungle in daylight would be visible to the enemy and subject to sniper fire and hasty ambushes. But he could put eyes out there where concealment was available. He had to settle for OPs close to the hill in daylight hours. With darkness they would move with great care to pre-selected positions further out and set up listening posts, the LPs. Meanwhile he would use air power to complicate NVA planning and preparation for their assault on his position.

The aircraft struck along likely avenues of approach to the blocking position. Finally, he traced a line from his position to the suspected location of the 66th Regiment earlier reported by the POWs. He had the aircraft concentrate fire along that line with Covey's help. There would be no telltale secondary explosions if the bombs found their mark, the bodies of men, but enemy soldiers would die in the dark jungle. Guesswork plus combat experience guided his actions.

He visited each platoon leader for face-to-face coordination. Fields of fire were confirmed, especially for the machine guns and recoilless rifles; mines were emplaced; and for the first time, the 81mm mortars were registered to fire killing ammunition instead of illumination rounds. Night vision devices were manned continuously.

An ominous report from Kontum indicated high probability that the weather was about to turn bad.

The next move in the set-piece battle on the Ho Chi Minh trail was up to the 66th NVA regiment. But meanwhile, the Hatchet Teams were active.

Robbie

Direct action was Robbie's natural inclination, just as Ridgerunner's was indirection. He aimed Jimmy in the direction of a well-used feeder trail leading to the main trail, a likely place for the enemy to hold vehicles until they could continue the trip south. Kingston brought up the rear. Robbie fell in directly behind Jimmy. They moved for little more than an hour when the faint sounds of motors promised that they would soon be in contact with the enemy.

It was hard to estimate the exact distance to the sound. Robbie directed Jimmy through dense jungle in the direction of the truck motor noises. Walking on any trail in the vicinity of good troops was suicidal. It invited ambush. Robbie, self-confident to the point of arrogance, knew he was up against good troops. But he also knew that a small team could rip apart logistical troops surprised and unprepared for close combat. Robbie saw his team as a shark among sea lion puppies, easy targets. But he had to penetrate enemy security. Then he intended to fight his way out before enemy sharks arrived.

NVA trackers and light infantry were good, so good that Robbie would have welcomed them to his RT. He was also pleased with his own troops, confident that they would be immediately responsive to his commands. He was very good, and he knew it. As a consequence, he had few friends in CCC, but he had admirers who could wonder at his gifts and skills while overlooking his arrogance. Connoisseurs of the art form wondered if Robbie or Waldron or Schaefer were the best killers in CCC. It was generally understood that Ridgerunner was the best pure recon man, but this situation called for killers. Robbie was a killer.

The rumble of motors stopped. From the sounds, Robbie assumed that vehicles had been tucked into safe places where they would wait until it was safe to continue their trip south.

Jimmy froze, raised his right hand, and gently lowered himself to a prone position. He aimed his silenced grease gun to his one o'clock. Robbie glided to Jimmy's right shoulder as the team faced outward for all-around security without a sound or signal. Jimmy touched his ear. It wasn't necessary. Robbie heard the voices. Kingston had moved to a position providing direct eye contact with Robbie, when the team leader looked back. Robbie touched his own ear, pointed to the sound of voices, pointed to himself and Jimmy, circled his right hand held high, and pointed to Kingston, who bobbed his head. The team leader and point man were to check out the sounds ahead. The rest of the team would remain in place under Kingston's control.

Robbie and Jimmy slithered to the sound of voices and giggles. The targets were oblivious to danger. Through the vegetation, Robbie saw the backs of two unarmed soldiers sitting on the bank overlooking a road on which the tops of parked trucks were visible. The soldiers faced the trucks talking, eating, and laughing. They were holding hands the way many Vietnamese men did, causing Americans to jump to the possibly wrong conclusion. Behind the two soldiers were sleeping rolls. No weapons were in sight. Robbie estimated that the soldiers were truck drivers relaxing until they were told to get rolling. There seemed to be no assembly or bivouac area. The trucks were bumper to bumper. Apparently the drivers slept in the trucks or beside them.

The relaxed atmosphere told Robbie that he was among the sea lion puppies that were hidden from attack from the sky and unaware of sharks in the local water. But somewhere out there was the enemy's first team. When Robbie acted, the enemy security force would close in. How much time would he have?

He assessed the situation.

The drivers strung along the road and on the trucks, he reasoned, can't conduct a coordinated counterattack on the RT. Enemy leaders wouldn't be able to round up truck drivers to concentrate an effective reaction to rapid and violent action. On the other hand, he'd have to deal with random gaggles of logistics soldiers in unknown locations. Some of them will grab weapons, screw up their courage, and take pot shots at the RT, once the initial shock wears off. That will produce some casualties in the team. And then getting out? Once the shit hits the fan, the security troops—pissed at having failed to protect the puppies—will come after us. It boiled down to go/no go. Now.

It always does, thought Robbie. Combat may begin with vision, a good plan, a sound concept, but it quickly becomes a series of go/no go decisions by the combat leaders on the scene managing accidents. Most decisions in ordinary human experience are softer, gentler, ambiguous, varied, subtle, and revocable. Often they just don't really matter. Some are non-decisions that produce consequences through indecision. That was the critical difference between war and peace. Decide life and death now—that's war. Sort things out next week-month-year-decade—that's peace. Make it happen now is war; go with the flow is peace. Decisions in close combat are final—for someone. This was an exceedingly dangerous situation.

Robbie loved it.

***

He and Jimmy backed off to allow Robbie to do some thinking and some talking on the radio.

Question to himself: Do something or nothing?

Answer: Easy. Something.

Question: Direct action, or use air first?

Answer: He glanced at the thick canopy overhead. If I use air first, the trucks might disperse before I can adjust the strikes. Give Covey a fix on my location with smoke, since I have no reference point in this jungle seen from the air as a sea of green. I might be duking it out with the 66th and unable to control air assets. If I go at it direct, I can put a bad hurt on the enemy and destroy a dozen trucks real quick and make one hell of a traffic jam on the constricted road. Probably no way for them to by-pass. I can drop smoke for follow-on air strikes as we destroy trucks and kill drivers. That's the solution: alert Covey, shoot up convoy—close, personal and direct—put air on the target. Get out and away from the road. Air can pound the target and cover our breakout. Go for it.

Robbie asked Covey how soon he could have strike aircraft overhead. Covey had a string on tac air; the answer was five minutes. So much for the larger issue. Now Robbie turned to the immediate situation. Instead of a cute, complex plan that invited error, Robbie kept it basic, insuring that each man understood what he was to do. That was the Fort Benning KISS formula: Keep It Simple, Stupid. Then he executed.

He and Jimmy led the way back to the two giggling truck drivers who died happy as Jimmy killed them with bursts from his silenced grease gun at a range of five yards. They never knew what hit them. The RT lined up along the near side of the road. The 57mm recoilless rifle initiated the noisy action by hitting the most distant visible truck to the left under Robbie's direction. A second later the M-60 machine gun, under Kingston's control out of the back blast area to the right of the RT skirmish line, engaged the visible trucks furthest to the right. The rest of the team used their CAR-15s and M-79 grenade launchers to rake the trucks to the direct front. Within minutes the recoilless rifle destroyed six trucks to the left with shots aimed at their engines. A secondary explosion rang the ears of the team. The machine gun traced a trail through the trucks and into drivers in the trucks and on the road. Kingston moved the machine gun fire from right to left and back again using bursts of six until 500 rounds were fired. The sound of his gun drowned out the cries of a shocked enemy unaccustomed to the violence of close combat.

Two Montagnards moved to the nearest trucks to place thermite grenades on their engine blocks. The grenades burned with a white heat, literally passing through the engine blocks. In the first four or five minutes of the action, the only weapons' fire came from the RT. Robbie, Kingston, and two Montagnards pulled pins on smoke grenades and pitched them onto the road on Robbie's command. Shock was complete. So far the enemy was paralyzed. Robbie told Covey to look for tracers and fired upward through the thinnest canopy.

"Robbie, I have a fix on your tracers."

"Covey, mark it. When your marking round burns down, mark it again. I need about zero five to get out of the target area. You should see my smoke."

After a short pause, "Rog. I see green smoke. Wilco on marking. Wadda we got?"

"Roger, green. A traffic jam. Destroyed a dozen trucks, maybe twenty, bumper to bumper. Unknown how far the column extends north and south from my location."

"Roger."

"You'll get secondaries. Just keep working out from center of mass. This trail is full of trucks."

"Rog."

"I'm gonna go northeast to break contact and evade. If you don't hear me in zero-five, put strikes on your mark."

"Rog."

As Covey coordinated the strike birds, Robbie moved. To make speed, he got on the road. He moved at a slow run along the right side of the column of trucks. Kingston kept pace with Robbie on the other side of the trucks. The first two Yards on either side of the trucks alternated to reload and keep constant fire on the enemy as they ran down the road. The road bent to the right. Robbie and Kingston saw an unbroken line of vehicles parked bumper to bumper. Robbie extended his arms parallel to the ground left and right to put the team on line. Kingston directed the machine gun that ripped rounds into the most distant trucks to prevent escape from the killing zone as the team poured death into the closer vehicles and people. When each man had fired two or three magazines into the bunched trucks and men ahead, Robbie broke left leading the team into the jungle on the far side of the road. He waved Kingston through to lead the team at a right angle to the trail while he spoke into his radio.

"Covey, Robbie."

"Covey."

"Trucks parked bumper to bumper continue for at least two zero zero meters northeast of your marker. I'm going west into bush to break contact. Give me two minutes, zero-two, to get out of target area. Then light up the trail. Moving. Out."

Robbie brought up the rear. Kingston put space between the team and the road. It wasn't long before he heard the familiar sound of impact to his rear as bombs fell. The welcomed sound of explosions confirmed the calculus: little boom, gas tank; big boom, munitions. There were lots of booms. As he moved behind his team away from the sound of explosions, he was satisfied even as he knew that the worst was ahead of them.

He had hit the jackpot. Recon men dreamed about putting accurate friendly fire on a big, static target like the one being worked over right now. The Air Force will see ever more targets by hitting vehicles and blasting away the concealing jungle.

The team was in danger. They had been lucky to get to the target without tangling with the enemy's first team, lucky to actually see the trail and the vehicles, lucky to run along it for a peek around the curve, and lucky to have shocked the logistics troops into inaction. Most of all, they were lucky not to be slowed down by casualties. Not a scratch. Yet.

The initial success confirmed Robbie's personal conviction based upon a lot of killing. Brief, violent, shock action is the best tool in the combat leader's bag of tricks. It rendered the enemy numb and incapable of reasoned reaction, and it allowed the aggressive force, fueled by adrenaline, to maintain the initiative. But now his team was in the middle of an enemy logistical complex surrounded by good NVA troops and dying bad soldiers. The enemy would be after them as the dust settled. Worse. The enemy would be covering every LZ and trail in his backyard. Trackers would soon see where the RT turned off the main trail. Ahead of them ambushes would be set up. For now his plan was simply to stay off trails and discourage trackers while Covey found an extraction site. That plan was the best of shitty alternatives. Robbie was keenly aware that his enemy knew the AO like a good salesman knows his territory. For the moment, even in bad trouble, he savored the sounds of success as the bombs fell ever further to his rear.

Covey was methodically extending strikes from the initial target marked by Robbie's tracers. Robbie saw the entire scene in his mind's eye, as he shook the wait-a-minute vines from his body and weapons as he drove on. The burning and exploding vehicles told Covey to keep working in the path of destruction. When he came up empty in one direction, Covey would work the strike birds down the trail in the other direction. The pilots could admire their handiwork. Most of them had put lots of holes in the sky and burned lots of jungle, never knowing the results of their efforts but suspecting their futility. Today Uncle Sam got his money's worth. Uncle Ho was having a bad day at the office.

The strike was still producing secondaries thirty minutes later when Robbie tapped the butt of the Yard in front of him. Each man in turn tapped the man to his front until Kingston got the word. Robbie moved forward to join Kingston. He was brief.

"I lead. We stay off trails. Put a trip wire Claymore here. We change direction. Should be bad guys on our ass. Can't miss our track. Next stop, we ambush."

Kingston nodded. Standard operating procedures obviated the need for much explaining. If Robbie took the lead, Kingston became tail gunner. If Kingston took the lead, Robbie did some dirty work in the rear. Robbie gave Covey his change in direction. Then he moved out.

Minutes later Robbie smiled when the Claymore detonated.

Trackers are close; that will slow them down, he thought. Gives 'em something to think about as they take the next step. Gets a man to thinking about just how exposed his balls and belly are.

He studied the terrain as he moved. On a gentle rise, he looked back to satisfy himself that he had line of sight for almost twenty meters. In another twenty meters he stopped, set up all around security, and took three Claymores, one each from three Yards. He and Jimmy backtracked, placed the mines off the trail, oriented on the back trail. He set them up for command detonation. He did that by inserting wires into each mine. Those wires were connected to a single wire that he ran back to where the RT waited. Jimmy concealed the wires. When Robbie stopped, he nodded. Jimmy went back to the mines, pulled the safety pins, insuring that the wires were hidden. They waited.

The team was on the little rise, prepared to put it between the enemy and the route of withdrawal. Robbie and Jimmy were slightly to the side of the track the team had made as it passed, and closest to pursuers. Jimmy studied the covered route he and Robbie would use to loop back to the RT after the ambush. The plan was simple. Robbie's plans were always simple. He would execute the ambush by pressing a device held in one of his hands, thus detonating three directional mines simultaneously. The effect was like a dozen shotguns firing double-0 shot at once. Immediately after the blast, Kingston would direct the fires of the M-60 machine gun just beyond the blast area to inflict further casualties on the enemy behind the point men. The fire would also allow Robbie and Jimmy to take a looping route back to the RT under cover of the machine gun fire.

Fifteen minutes after the Claymores were positioned, Robbie saw four bodies blown aside like newspapers in a strong wind after he squeezed the clacker. He assumed that more enemy troops further back in the column were hit. After several bursts from the M-60, the team was reunited and moved out.

The enemy was hurt. Pursuit continued.

Until the RT heard trucks, there was no way to know of the trail ahead. It appeared on no map. Robbie deduced that his pursuers were in radio contact with the their friends to his front. Bad shit. These soldiers would not be giggling truck drivers happily oblivious to danger. He had hunters on his tail and killer teams on the trucks ahead. He was their target.

Robbie moved 45 degrees to his left to avoid being pinched front and rear. The sound of an M-60 behind him was answered by an AK-47. That was Kingston covering their back trail. The good news was that the American fired first. The bad news was that despite his efforts to delay them, the trackers were pressing. Hard. The silence from the trucks meant that troops ahead were doing just what he would do: they had dismounted and were moving to the sound of the guns.

He put himself in their shoes, thinking how many times he had played both sides of this hunter-killer game in North Carolina, Florida, Bavaria, Korea, Okinawa, and in the UK. The concept was simple: trackers drove the hunted into a net. The NVA troops who had jumped off the trucks were forming an extended line to his front—the net—to intercept Robbie & Co. Once the net made contact with the RT, it was just a matter of time before the relative strengths of the forces engaged would result in the annihilation of the team as it fought in two directions in the middle of the jungle out of sight of Covey. Robbie's counter was also simple in concept, but it was difficult to execute because of the aggressive pursuit of the trackers. Clearly, the enemy was prepared to spend lives to kill the American team in his midst.

Robbie changed direction to avoid being caught between a hammer and an anvil. He could try to slip left or right, or he could make a gross change in direction in an attempt to break contact. Slipping around the line presumably forming to his right front wouldn't work. The close pursuit and the radio he guessed the enemy was using—it was more than coincidence that the troops had unassed the trucks dead ahead—meant that the tenacious little bastards were on his ass, talking to their friends forming the anvil. He did the quintessential Robbie thing. He moved back to set up a skirmish line under Kingston. The 57mm recoilless rifle was put to work. He intended to use all 57mm ammo; then he would spike the weapon. Yards on line stopped the pursuers with heavy automatic fire, but two Montagnards were hit, one seriously. Robbie told Kingston to withdraw by bounds: part of

Kingston's element would delay the enemy with fire while another part moved to the rear. The support element then fired while the others leap-frogged further to the rear.

The wounded compounded Kingston's problems by slowing movement. The Yard with a flesh wound in his side also had a possible broken rib, but he was still effective as a fighter. The Yard with a hole in his chest was a different matter. His poncho was wrapped around his chest and secured with suspension line over a bandage to close the sucking wound. He had to be carried piggyback, a treatment that might kill him, but there weren't enough people to fight off the enemy while caring for him properly.

While Kingston's element of the RT engaged the force biting at its heels, Robbie took an M-60 and half the team with him. He moved in the direction from which they had just come, parallel to his original track. As the trackers focused on Kingston, Robbie hooked back to hit them in the flank with machine gun fire, M-79s, and CAR-15s. Robbie blew his shrill whistle, the signal for the whole RT to advance on the trackers. The hunters had become the hunted, but Robbie felt a sting in his left arm and another Yard went down with blood leaking through the trousers covering his left upper leg. Two team members now had to be carried, and two were walking wounded, including Robbie. The trackers were surprised to be so boldly struck at the front and on their left flank by an aggressive force that should have been on the run. The 57mm fire was particularly effective. It was also disconcerting, since it suggested a force far more potent than the light recon teams the NVA had been chasing for years. The shock of heavy, well-aimed fire from two directions caused the NVA trackers to recoil and regroup.

The NVA troops moving to contact from the road ahead had been left out of the show as Robbie turned on his tormentor, a neat little example of divide and conquer. The team killed six enemy troops and blood trails suggested a few more had been dragged off, but now the RT could hear movement from the direction of the road. The NVA soldiers who had set up the anvil were now moving to the sound of the firefight as Robbie evaluated his enemy and gave him good marks. Robbie admired craftsmen.

He told Kingston to take the point and to lead the team again at a right angle from the previous direction of march in the hope that the two enemy elements would get in a firefight with one another. Robbie and Jimmy took up a position at the rear of the RT, engaged the trackers and fired in the direction of movement from the road. As the two enemy units returned fire, Robbie and Jimmy moved in the direction of the RT. The ruse worked for a few minutes, but the NVA quickly assessed the situation and resumed the hunt. The team was slowed by the need to carry two wounded men.

All members of the team had been stealing glances upward even while firing and moving. The Yard behind Kingston smiled and pointed upward and off to the right. Kingston saw it too, a glimpse of blue sky through the green ceiling. Kingston stopped under the hole in the jungle until joined by Robbie. The one-zero quickly registered that enemy pursuit was too close and too determined to allow a string extract from this point. But, thought Robbie, at last I can give Covey a fix on my location.

As he called Covey, he signaled for 360-degree security. Covey had a rough notion where the team was, but before its precise location could be ascertained another intense firefight erupted. Kingston needed to buy time for Robbie. He grabbed two Montagnards and formed a three-man skirmish line. The M-60 and two CAR-15s on full automatic poured into the enemy, but the disciplined trackers, sensing RT desperation, responded in kind.

Kingston, hit in the head, was dead before his body struck the jungle floor. One of the Montagnards went down clutching his stomach. The fire superiority of the enemy was evident to Robbie. He expected a final assault at any moment.

"Covey, I mark with tracers," said Robbie, inserting an all-tracer magazine into his weapon.

"Roger."

"Short count: five, four, three, two, one, tracers!"

On the final word, he fired the tracers.

Delay. Then, "I got tracers, Robbie."

"Mark it, Covey."

"Roger. Are you coming out on strings?"

"Negative. Mark for strike."

"Roger. Mark for strike. What is your direction of movement?"

"Negative movement. My one-one is down, and I got five WIA. Put strike on tracers."

There was a pause as Covey digested that transmission.

"I say back for possible correction. Put air strike on tracers."

"Rog. Do it."

"Wilco."

Robbie heard the marking round splash into the canopy to his right front and noted the increased tempo of enemy fire. He quickly dropped a thermite grenade into the 57mm recoilless rifle and personally fired the M-60 machine gun at the green-tan figures now five to ten meters in front of him. He could only make out three of his Yards firing, but some of the green-tan figures fell. He was firing a disciplined series of bursts of six rounds and watching good soldiers die when he experienced a kind of flash of light and saw expanding and shrinking concentric circles.

A Montagnard took the machine gun from the fallen Robbie and got off two bursts before he was shot. The last Montagnard tossed a grenade at advancing NVA troops, but he was shot dead before he had the satisfaction of seeing three enemy soldiers go down in the flash of the grenade explosion.

"Robbie, this is Covey."

Covey repeated the call three times before saying,

"Kingston, this is Covey."

There was no response.

***

The lieutenant of the 66th Regiment pulled the radio handset from the hand of the big American, held it high, and smiled at his soldiers looking at him. They smiled back and resumed their search of the bodies around them. The lieutenant took Robbie's watch and the gold chain from his neck. He could read the English inscribed in the heavy gold medallion. It said: "Fuck Communism."

The radio spoke again. Smiling either at the futile radio calls or at the message on Robbie's gold chain, he saw the napalm canister explode directly above him, releasing a flood of flaming goo that stuck to him and his soldiers. The expression on Robbie's face was a smile or a grimace as the RT and the NVA soldiers burned. Together.

CHAPTER TWELVE

Joe's Ambush

The Main Body

"I didn't think it could happen to Robbie. After surviving ten wounds, I thought he was superman. I don't know of anyone shot more than Robbie," said Ken Key.

"I guess I thought if anybody would come out of this son of a bitch, he would. Other guys died. Not Robbie."

"You weren't the only one," a commo man chimed in.

Neither Day nor a second commo man spoke, but they nodded assent. Robbie was invincible. More than a man had died. In a small tribe, news of the demise of a legend travels fast. Icons don't die. Some of the cockiness went out of the tribe. That might have started after Fat Albert's mission.

"Nothin' confirmed," said the first commo man.

"Yeah. He's MIA," said the second.

"Rog. Missing In Action," said the third.

"That's right," said Key.

Each of them knew better. But officially, until his body was found, he was MIA. Not KIA.

Day was surprised at his personal reaction. He didn't want to reveal how deeply moved he was as the faces of dead and living recon men paraded through his memory. He could see them all. Ridgerunner had barely gotten out. Thank God. Robbie hadn't. Grady had sacrificed himself when he marked the target with his tracer rounds.

They had put their asses on the line without fanfare.

A profound sadness overcame him. Memories of a previous tour in Vietnam recalled other good men gone. Now, skilled soldiers in Kontum; then, conscripts in C Company, 27th Infantry in Korea, one of them losing a leg at the age of twenty. More good men. Gone.

"Bad vibes," he thought as a premonition grabbed him.

"We'll never be the same."

It was a good thing that he didn't reveal his true feelings in his depressed state. Losing Robbie was a shock. He was prepared to call the whole goddamn thing off. It wasn't worth the loss of these wonderful men. And it wasn't over.

Despite willingly submerging himself in the collective identity of SF—he was truly a team player—Day remained convinced that the final moral arbiter was individual conscience. Neither the Army nor SF had ever asked him to violate his conscience. He was grateful for that. Other soldiers in other armies were less fortunate. Koestler's protagonist in "Darkness At Noon" was made to feel that he was a heretic because his conscience was not congruent with the Party's dictates of the moment. What went through the mind of a Wehrmacht officer who loved Germany and necessarily served Hitler to serve Germany? What about the Russian who loved Mother Russia and served Stalin? For all of its defects, the American system never asked him to do what he considered to be a sin. Maybe I have a lax conscience.

Day did not share these ruminations with his admirably pragmatic soldiers. But they were in his head even when his body was in the mud. He assumed others had private reservations and doubts.

Joe

Meanwhile, Joe Waldron was in the boonies prepared for contact with the enemy as soon as "Lion Tamer" was declared. Like Robbie, Joe was always ready for a fight. His team was closest to the 66th Regiment base camp, according to the prisoners interrogated at the blocking position. The Major confirmed that the battle noises Joe had heard in the distance were strikes called by Ridgerunner and Robbie. Because Joe asked—and because CCC practice was not to bullshit your buddies—Day told Joe, in veiled terms, that Ridgerunner's team was out OK, and Robbie's team was probably KIA. Joe didn't particularly like Robbie, but he knew that it took brave and skilled soldiers to bring Robbie down. He concluded that a man could get hurt out here.

Joe's plan was aggressive. He intended to sow confusion in the 66th in order to take some pressure off the defenders at the blocking position. If he got lucky, he could put some airstrikes on 'em. Without a few surprises to keep it off balance, the enemy would roll over the blocking force.

Had he slipped into a quiet AO, Joe could have snooped around until he caught his enemy asleep at the switch. But CCC activity in the past 24 hours assured a high state of NVA readiness. It might make more sense to have his targets come to him.

Joe was thinking through how he might kick some ass. He was a good recon man, a collector of information, perfectly willing to count things and take pictures of them. But his preference was to kill people and break things. He was also as flexible as a wet noodle. Reckoning that he was between some kind of enemy base camp and the friendly blocking force, he searched for and found a high-speed trail leading to the blocking force.

"Damned if that isn't an interstate heading from here to my favorite Major."

An exaggeration, but he had found his ambush site. Joe put the team under his One-One while he made a personal recon with his best Yard. Staying off the trail, he traced it by moving at a snail's pace parallel to it until he found what he wanted. Then he put the team in position to kill.

He had seen this set-up in his dreams, the other ones, the ones in which naked Asian women did not star. Joe was concealed just below the crest of a hill with two Soviet light machine guns and a U.S. 57mm recoilless rifle under his control. He was looking down at a trail that climbed gently to him. He could see a hundred yards down the trail, a very long way in a war characterized by firefights often conducted at five to ten meters. The terrain along the trail sloped sharply from his left to his right. The natural reaction of a soldier desiring to get off the trail would be to go down, to Joe's right.

Fifty meters to his rear he positioned an American with a radio and a Yard. They comprised one security team. Their task was to call him if the bad guys approached his reception committee from the wrong direction. One hundred and fifty meters straight ahead and out of sight was another two-man team, an American with a radio and a Yard. Their job was to tell Joe what was coming his way so that he could decide if he wanted to take it on or allow it to pass. They would count noses and report the distance between enemy soldiers climbing the gentle rise toward Joe's position.

To the right, parallel to the trail, was the reason that Joe selected this site. Upon initiation of the ambush, he expected the enemy to break out of the killing zone on the trail by moving to Joe's right, downhill. That's where he placed his deadly Claymore mines at eight to ten meter intervals. On recon missions he required each team member to carry a Claymore, primarily for the team's all-around security in an overnight position. When he was looking for trouble, each of his men carried two Claymores per man. Each mine was carefully placed and concealed—sighted uphill to avoid barriers, such as big trees or folds in the terrain that might offer protection to the enemy. Each was oriented so that its fan overlapped with the mines to the left and right. A wall of steel pellets would greet any enemy fleeing the fires of automatic weapons on the trail.

Joe held the clacker that would command detonate the mines in a deadly blast.

They waited.

The squelch broke twice. Enemy in sight.

Faster than it takes to say it, Joe thought: Radio, be Alaska One!

Alaska One was in the right direction to provide the early warning that would trigger the ambush. Alaska Two was the security team to his rear.

"Zero, One."

"Good," thought Joe. He said, "Go, One."

"Two man point. No flank security. Main body ten meters back. Sling arms. Two-zero and counting. Wait."

***

The cryptic message told Joe that he was about to score a big kill. The distance between the point and the main body indicated that the enemy was fat, dumb and happy, more concerned with speed than security. The NVA force was on a stroll in its own back yard. Sling arms meant not even minimum readiness. The enemy had committed the cardinal sin of a combat soldier: he felt secure.

"Joe, five-zero and counting. Single file. Bunched."

Joe saw movement to his front that became the two-man point some 100 meters straight ahead. He cut the squelch and spoke.

"Two, did you monitor?"

"Two. Roger.

"One and Two, I initiate. I got the point."

"One. Roger."

"Two. Rog."

***

Initiation of the ambush by the commander was SOP, but Joe taking out the point was not. Normally he would have permitted the point to walk through the ambush site to be dispatched by the security team to his rear. Because the enemy owned this real estate, his point was actually part of the main body. The first man should have been fifty yards ahead of his buddies. The second man in the point should have had visual contact to the first man and the main body. They were too close to one another, a fatal error.

At fifty meters Joe could see the camouflage capes, some of cloth and some of fresh-cut branches. The capes sat on their shoulders and rucksacks as they walked. Their main concern was detection from the air. At the sound of aircraft each man would halt as he pulled his cape over his head and body and remained motionless. Along this stretch of trail the thick overhead jungle canopy hid them from observation from above. That probably explained their carelessness. They felt safe.

"Joe, One. I got eight-zero and counting."

"Rog. When I execute, you displace to me."

"Rog. At nine-zero and counting."

Joe knew he had a company in front of him. Maybe a battalion. Point men twenty meters. Ten meters. They never glanced at Joe.

Nineteen, twenty years old. Soft brown eyes. Some whiteness on their uniforms under the armpits. Salt. One typical slender Vietnamese. The other unusually well built. He heard voices. He saw them smiling at something the slender one said.

"Big mistake," he thought as he held the slender one in his AK sights.

"Pay attention, soldier."

A round in the sternum. Center of mass. He put two rounds there and moved to a second sternum with two more. As the point men fell, Joe heard his two machineguns scream. One fired at the nearest enemy troops, and the other started at the most distant. Bursts of six. Bursts of six. Again and again. From the ends of the column to the middle the light machine gun tore into flesh and bone. Superimposed on that rhythm was the crack of the 57mm rifle. The gunner started a third of the way down the column and worked his way to the end of the trail. Firing as fast as his assistant loaded, the gunner fired round after round every ten meters. In addition to the fire of the crew-served weapons, each of Joe's men fired his individual weapon.

Joe watched the carnage. Those who didn't fall to the machine guns and the 57 jumped down the slope. He detonated his mines. The roar greeted those spared from death on the trail with thousands of metal bits. Stirring bodies were raked with machine gun fire.

The ambush was less than two minutes old when a hundred young men sighed their last breaths.

"Joe, this is One. I see another six-zero and counting."

Joe estimated that he had hit the lead element of an NVA battalion. A hundred plus sixty plus whatever trailed the sixty.

"One, c'mon in. Haul ass."

Just as the American said, "Rog," the Montagnard with him on Alaska One saw three NVA troopers with bazooka-like B-40s taking up positions to put their rounds on Joe Waldron. From 100 meters with an open trail to guide on, they couldn't miss. Even a miss of fifteen meters would produce wounds. The Yard dropped two of them. The American shot the third. Their position revealed, they attracted a high volume of fire from the enemy who had not entered the killing zone. The friendlies fell. The Yard was dead. Using fire and movement, the enemy troops closed with and killed the wounded American.

The quick reaction of NVA troops pressing forward was no surprise to Joe, but their numbers were. He regarded the NVA as the best light infantry in the world. The battle noises out of sight to his front told him that his forward security team was in serious trouble.

Joe instructed his gunners to fall back. As they took their first steps, another trio of B-40s moved forward and fired into Joe's position. Joe, his machine gunners, and the 57 crew were wounded with shrapnel from the B-40 grenades, some seriously. The B-40 gunners reloaded and fired again and again. In conjunction with the continuous rocket fire, enemy troops were beginning to flank Joe from the high ground to his left. Joe smiled ruefully as he noted that he wasn't the only guy in Laos with quick reaction drills. He noted also the thumping sound of M-79 launchers being used by friendlies and the enemy. More and more the enemy was using U.S. weapons and equipment. The enemy hadn't had time to plan. The NVA leaders were now getting the pay-off from drill and training—and some equipment Made in America.

Joe assessed his situation. Two of his Yards were seriously hit, and all of his people, except for the rear security team, were wounded. He called the security team. "Two, Joe."

"Joe, this is Two."

"Two, execute Echo-Echo."

"Rog. See you at Romeo Peter."

"Negative. Press on to primary Lima Zulu."

Joe had told the security team to execute the team Escape and Evasion plan. The security man said he'd meet Joe at the pre-selected Rally Point, where, under normal circumstances, Joe would have accounted for everyone before continuing to move. Joe said, no. Get the hell out. He had directed his subordinate to save himself and the Montagnard.

Joe had told Covey that he was setting up an ambush, but he hadn't given Carpenter a confirmed fix on his location. Covey presence would have risked blowing the ambush. Now it didn't matter. Whatever his fate, Joe wanted to hurt the enemy.

Not this time. Before he could guide the Covey bird to his location, he was engaged in close combat with a foe pumping rockets on him as riflemen with AKs closed in on the band of wounded Alaska men from the front and left flank. The CCC men went down swinging, but they went down. The last thing Joe saw was the man he killed and the other man, the one who killed Joe.

***

The NVA force tended to its wounded, sending the ambulatory to the rear, and buried its dead. The enemy junior leaders executed the American and Montagnard wounded before resuming the march to reinforce the assault on the American blocking force.

Now, the enemy commander put out flank security. The point was well ahead of the main body. Soldiers maintained an interval of five yards between men. Their weapons were in their hands, at the ready. Experience is the best teacher.

One American and one Yard from Joe's RT executed the escape and evasion plan.

CHAPTER THIRTEEN

End Game: The Politics

First Amendment Blues

Fred knew his masters. The editors in New York ran PJ's story on page one, under an eye-catching lead: "U.S. Wages Secret War in Laos." PJ's copy was barely touched by rewrite. The kid could write.

His eyewitness reporting rang true. He described inherently exciting action in the context of factual background material, the fruits of earlier research. The political implications were obvious and serious. Johnson and Nixon had conducted a secret war using Special Forces soldiers sponsored earlier by John Kennedy, who gave them their Green Beret. The U.S. Government, under Johnson and Nixon, continued to lie routinely to the American people. The important story was skillfully presented at a time when Americans were tired of the war in Vietnam, tired of racial strife at home, and tired of accepting responsibility for all sorts of foreigners from places they never heard of and couldn't locate on a map. Public opinion about the war in Vietnam had meandered from blissful ignorance to tacit acceptance to general opposition.

Several teasers were seeded in PJ's story. They promised more to follow in a series that would reveal the unholy alliance of Special Forces and the CIA; lies by public officials in the name of confidentiality; infiltration teams lost in North Vietnam; Navy SEAL participation in SOG missions; assassination teams and other dirty tricks aimed at enemy infrastructure; envy among conventional troops and general purpose forces regarding elite units getting the lion's share of support; mysterious black U.S. Air Force aircraft dedicated to SOG; dramatic missions conducted by super soldiers; and high rates of killed or missing in action among SOG personnel in Laos. All of this was revealed to a public asking why Americans were dying in a faraway place whose corrupt public officials owned Swiss bank accounts and whose soldiers who couldn't or wouldn't fight while American boys died.

"This yarn has spies, lies, envy, violence, corruption, just what a reader needs with his morning coffee," noted Fred.

The story concluded by calling SOG's blocking force the biggest battle of the secret war. An unnamed reliable source told the reporter "… everything that flies is committed to the fight in Laos." The reporter expected casualties that would be ascribed to actions in Vietnam "near the border" with Laos. In fact, the American casualties were produced "over the fence" in Laos.

From an editorial point of view, Fred admired the piece. It was good copy. The last paragraph left the reader begging for more. Good hook. The battle was the biggest. It promised to be bloody. If it bleeds, it leads. The nefarious government would hide the bodies. Neat stuff. The side bar at the beginning of the page-one piece alerted the reader to the series that would appear in the coming days. Nice touch. Another good hook. This is the stuff that wins prizes.

But Fred worried about the U.S. troops now hanging on by a tenuous thread facing a tough foe. Cripes! The enemy hides his every move, while we put current ops on page one. But isn't a free press one of the major differences between their system and ours? And isn't the quest for truth the very essence of good journalism? Hasn't my government lied to us? Aren't the MACV Public Affairs Officers propagandists?

"General Giap could fire his intelligence people and use my

newspaper to find out what SOG is up to."

***

Two communications from New York guided the Saigon bureau. One was an "Attaboy" to PJ. It stroked him and expressed confidence in his ability to produce the in-depth series on SOG that would follow his "first rate news story." The second message directed Fred to take PJ off all other assignments. The hero of the day was to concentrate on the SOG story. Unlimited research assistance was made available to PJ in Saigon from Washington, New York, or wherever a document or human source needed to be run down. The resources of a great newspaper were at the disposal of the new kid on the block.

"Good call," opined the craftsman in Fred. "If I were an editor in New York, that's what I'd do."

Having said that, he resented being told the obvious. "The officious pricks! Don't teach me how to suck eggs!"

Not for the first time in human history, the field man felt that the staffers at headquarters had convinced themselves that they communicated directly with God, while field guys were adolescents.

"Pricks," he said without passion.

***

PJ was elated. Instant celebrity was his. So was status among peers. And friends. Smile for the camera. Hi, mom! He'd cracked the big time. The news story was picked up in every corner of the world, and a steady outpouring of political commentary began to fill op-ed pages. People he had long studied and admired were commenting on his story! Heady stuff. Somehow the idea that the wire services around the globe had picked up his story excited him most. His stuff was being read in Paris and Hong Kong! Cairo and Ottawa! Boston and Dakar!

PJ also knew that he had opened Pandora's box. Some unintended consequences would surely follow his story and his feature series on SOG. Editorials and letters to editors from friends of America would express shock, disappointment, and shame. Professional scolds would be out in force. America haters would have a wonderful time with the revelations. He hadn't intended to hurt his country. But he did. He raised a question that demanded an answer. How could the United States wage a secret war all these years, lie about it, and still be "of the People"? He regretted the damage to his country and to special ops friends. But, he concluded, you can't make an omelet without breaking eggs.

Old Guy and Daring Young Man

Pietro thought he was a dead man. He wouldn't have been the first old campaigner to come through WWII, Korea, the Congo, a long list of unreported clandestine missions and many jumps from perfectly functioning aircraft only to find an end by riding a bird into a mountain or splashing into the jungle. Flying by helicopter from Kontum to Dak To, he experienced the worst weather he had ever seen in country. Considering the changeable weather patterns that he had seen in Vietnam's Central Highlands, that was a strong statement. In soldier speak, it was bad shit.

Pietro wondered how this adventure would compare to flying a helicopter through the falls at Niagara. Or running a 100-yard dash through a minefield in snowshoes—at night. Or free falling without a parachute.

En route from Kontum to the launch site, the rain had built until it was a solid wall. The old soldier wondered how the hell the kid pilot would find the landing pad at Dak To. What was the young stud thinking about? Had it dawned on him yet that he was mortal? Were these frightened old man thoughts? And once the kid found the pad, if he found the pad, how the hell could he put the bird on the ground so that they walked away from it rather than being scraped from it or fried in it? Too many good guys had crashed and burned in this goddamned war, voting with their bodies despite churning guts, dry mouths, and white knuckles. They wanted to do the right thing, whatever the hell that was. The kids, pilots or ground pounders, took to flight naturally. Older men loaned their bodies to the activity because it was the only way to stay in the game. But they didn't like it. Some call this duty.

At moments of great danger Pietro wrapped himself in a bubble of tranquility and trusted in God and in the soldier calling the shots at the moment. Sometimes that was Pietro. This time it wasn't.

This final approach to Dak To wasn't the first time Pietro's life was in the hands of a comrade. He kept his lips buttoned and glanced at his pilot, thinking:

"How old is he? Couldn't be much more than 21. Probably hasn't voted yet. Born when I was in Korea? He's about the age of my boy?"

In fact, the pilot had extended his second tour in Vietnam. He had done the same thing in his first tour, adding evidence to Pietro's thesis that combat is addictive. Combat infantry assaults were wild, but according to the kid pilot, nothing compared to flying for SOG. The recon men were his brothers. Wasn't nothin' that could keep him from plucking an RT out of the shit.

The kid lived for the moment: to rescue friends from death in the jungle, to fly, to buy women in Bangkok, Taipei, and Singapore. He said he wasn't really interested in the round eyes in Australia. Sure, he liked the Aussies he met in Vietnam, the men, but when it came to women he preferred that Asian stuff every time. Pietro remembered words like that from pals of the 1940s, 1950s, and 1960s. Hell, the Brits said things like that in the last century. Kipling knew a lot about east and west and soldiers and flying fishes. Many SF men were attracted to Okinawa, Korea, and Japan. Americans in 1970 were relearning what British, French and Dutch soldiers could have told them. Muck around in the East and you won't come out the same man.

The kid's voice broke Pietro's reverie:

"Circus Tent, this is Spad 4 inbound with Barnum 6, over."

The man on radio watch at Dak To had been told by Kontum launch team to expect the chopper with Pietro, the big boss, at about this time.

"Spad 4, Circus Tent, go!"

The pilot waxed poetic.

"Glad you're home, ol' buddy. I got zero viz and shit in my drawers. Request your assistance."

"You got it. Wadda ya need?"

"If I flew this bird good, you should hear my engine soon. If you don't, I can't tell what next."

213

"Rog. Wait."

The radio operator alerted everyone in the camp to listen for the blind incoming bird.

"Spad 4, all at this location listening for you."

The tension on the ground and in the bird was palpable. Two minutes passed.

"Spad 4, we hear you. Turn left a little bit, and look left for vehicle headlights."

The Dak To camp commander directed all trucks and jeeps to orient toward the sound of the chopper and turn on bright headlights. After several of the longest minutes ever recorded by man, the pilot spoke.

"Circus Tent, I see a glow like Yankee Stadium for a night game. Many thanks. Leave 'em on. Gotta feel for the ground. I sure as shit can't see it."

The pilot spoke to Pietro on the internal net:

"Colonel, cinch your lap and chest straps real tight. I can't see shit. If we bang in, release seat belt and roll out when we stop moving. Don't wait for me. Get away from bird and fuel."

"Wilco. Go for it."

The pilot smiled to himself. Game old fart.

Pietro looked left, right, ahead, and to the rear for sign of the ground or anything other than opaque grayness. The rainwater streamed down the bubble surrounding the pilots, and the windshield wipers moved double time as the pilot felt for the ground in slow motion. Pietro could see no more than a foot or two beyond the Plexiglas bubble. For government work, that was zero viz.

Suddenly he discerned a different feel as the downward and forward movement became something else. The colonel sensed rather than saw what the pilot was doing. He had caught the right skid in concertina wire and was trying to shake it off! At a demonstration on Armed Forces Day or the 4th of July several years earlier, Pietro had seen a bird decorated as Bozo the Clown push and blow a large ball up and down a field to entertain a crowd at Fort Benning. He thought of that as the kid pilot shook off the wire that fell to the ground, backed the bird up, and ever so gently put the aircraft on the red mud, more or less on the helipad.

He shut down.

Smiling, Pietro shook the young man's hand, saying:

"Mrs. Pietro and the kids thank you. That was impressive flying. Well done."

The pilot gave him a goofy grin as they waited for the rain to ease up. Scared shitless and soaked in telltale perspiration, he had his image to maintain:

"You call, we haul, Colonel. Ain't no big thing." Thing was pronounced "thang," hillbilly fashion.

As they caught their breath in the dryness of the small bird, American warriors of two generations entertained their private thoughts. The old guy thought about the American blocking force now denied its ace in the hole by the weather, air power. The young guy thought about the charms of Asian women.

Higher Headquarters

A wet, wrung out, but living Pietro joined Radich and Burns in the Dak To command post bunker. The old soldiers shared coffee while updating each other on the special operations community before reviewing the current situation. They then came to some conclusions.

First, the mission was already a success. The blocking force had interrupted enemy resupply to their forces in RVN. Robbie and Ridgerunner had orchestrated destruction of an estimated one hundred trucks carrying ammo and general supplies. Joe Waldron had killed an undetermined number of reinforcing enemy troops before contact with him was lost. The blocking force itself had inflicted casualties, some 200-400 killed by air, possibly more. It was difficult to be exact, but by the standards of the entire war in Vietnam, these were major accomplishments. And friendly losses were heavy by SOG standards.

Second, current weather in the tri-border area favored the enemy. Air support, except radio relay, was impossible at the moment and unlikely in the next day or so. There was a substantial NVA presence in the area, and it would increase. The initial surprise was lost. In an old fashioned slugging match, the good guys could hurt the bad guys, but there was no doubt that the final outcome would find the NVA overrunning the blocking position.

Third, commanders on the ground could not know how political leadership would jump, now that the press had the story. The administration had egg on its face. What would the politicians do that would affect troops still on the ground? They may be the best and the brightest, but the inner sanctum of policy formulation consisted of men subject to the inherent frailty of the human condition. Like panic. And finger pointing. And limits in empathy. And CYA. When all else fails, Cover Your Ass.

Pietro concluded that his best course of action was to pick up his winnings and leave the table. An important part of any commander's mission is to preserve the force to fight another day. By taking action on the basis of tactical considerations he might avoid the consequences of a possibly hasty political decision by Washington whiz kids. Pietro feared decisions by men wearing suits. He confessed his strong preference for muddy boots soldiers.

Radich had never served on a political-military staff, nor was he politically sophisticated. He concurred for operational reasons. His men had milked this one for all it was worth. Once locked in a knock down, drag-out brawl, disengagement would be a bitch. When Roger Pietro ordered him to terminate the operation as soon as possible, Radich was not displeased.

Pietro informed Mark Burns of his decision. Burns recognized the soundness of the decision and notified his admiral in Hawaii. Pietro notified the SOG Commander, who would inform General Abrams.

***

Colonel John Plunkett sat at his gray desk, staring at gray chairs, gray safes, and several gray filing cabinets in the windowless J-2 shop of the Joints Chief of Staff at the very moment Pietro talked to Burns and Radich in Dak To. From behind the green door in this corner of the Pentagon, he couldn't know that Pietro had just decided to pull his troops back to Vietnam. But as the Joint Special Ops guy, he was sensitive to how clandestine military operations intersected with policy decisions at the very top of the government's hierarchy. Pietro and Radich would work the operational end of things. Machinations at the policy level tended to be more convoluted. Plunkett saw himself as the useful link between political and military authority. Faithful to the orders of his Commander-in-Chief, he would see that the soldiers were given every chance to get the job done—and survive.

The SOG story by a cub reporter reverberated up and down the so-called corridors of power. In fact, Pentagon corridors led to windowless caves, fast-food snack bars and toilets. Thus far, press inquiries were met with "no comment" at State, Defense, and the White House. But the questions wouldn't go away. Taking no for an answer was not the habit of the Washington press corps, particularly on a slow news day. Since a source would soon be found in any event—someone was always prepared to pop off for reasons ranging from nobility to venality—an official spokesman had to respond before the Laos story got out of hand. Getting bogged down with it could keep decision makers from governing. It could also mean that the man accustomed to his residence on Pennsylvania Avenue might not enjoy the perks or the grand old house for another four years.

Plunkett wasn't privy to the frantic analyses being conducted around town as officialdom cooked up a plausible response to PJ's story. Politicians would make that call. But he had been in the game so long that he reflexively worked the problem.

His part was simple, if painful. As the JSOA, he had to explain to the civilian masters what had happened. How did the Army fail to keep the operation from the press? The simple honest answer would not close the matter: a journalist ingratiated himself with real soldiers, got close to the action, did his homework, and used his good sense and skill to tell the story.

There would be a finger-pointing exercise. A gaggle of special ops colonels would hear the obvious: they wouldn't be generals. Since they hadn't expected stars in any event, that was not crushing news. Others—professional soldiers, whose orthodox careers predisposed them to be dubious about special ops—would say: I told you so. Mix military ops and politics and what you get is bad ops and bad politics. Some soldiers as well as civilians believed that dirty tricks and clandestine missions should be left to civilian spooks and operators. They had a point.

Plunkett knew that the witch-hunt in the Army would be fleeting noise in the background. A few SF heads might roll, but the tension between conventional soldiers and special ops true believers would continue. Legitimate differences about emphasis fueled vigorous debate among the uniformed types, but that was internal to the military. The public knew little of that debate and cared less. The hard questions would be directed at political authority.

He could hear the questions even as he sat in the gray-on-gray decor of his windowless cave mulling over what the operation in Laos would surface. Did U.S. Forces violate the neutrality of a non-belligerent? Who authorized the operations? How long has the U.S. been conducting ops in Laos? Did U.S. Forces violate the neutrality of other nations? Is that U.S. policy? Are U.S.-led forces in North Vietnam? Did the U.S. Government lie to the press? To allies? Are American troops in Laos now? Plunkett didn't envy the wordsmiths providing text for spokespersons who must walk the line between putting the best face on things and blatant lying. "No comment" would not suffice.

The President had authorized the blocking force in Laos; the White House must deny the President's involvement. Then, who authorized the mission? Do renegades make U.S. policy? When will they be fired? Or did the President tacitly approve? If not, when is the trial? If so, why did the President of the United States of America lie? Are there other examples of such lying? Just how long has this been going on? Solomon's wisdom was required. Liars outnumbered wise men in Washington—and everywhere else.

Jack smiled, thinking, "There's no shortage of lickspittles and Pinocchios in this town. Too many of them turn in a conscience for an ID card, power, or a vita entry."

He had read PJ Riley's story carefully and concluded that the writer had the military by the short hairs. He nailed SOG on the current operation, and the projected series promised to keep the story alive for weeks as other reporters fed on it. It had legs. Commentators on TV and on the editorial and op-ed pages will tell the public what to think about the news and feature stories. Jack thought, "Talking head retired soldiers and diplomats will add their voices to the noise produced by much nonsense and some wisdom. In the current political climate, there won't be many apologists for the government in the media."

Yep, the kid had his government by the short hairs. After a bad couple of years since Tet '68, it gets worse. How did that matron at the cocktail party put it? "Colonel, could you in good conscience recommend a military career to your favorite nephew?" Good question, lady.

"I'm glad this one isn't in my in-box," Plunkett mused, still staring unseeing at the fashion-statement furniture of his government while talking to himself. He reached for the phone, wondering if talking to himself was a sign of madness or an enlightened choice of audience.

"Time to talk to Karl in the White House. Poor man. But I need to see how decisions being kicked around at the top might affect our guys on the ground."

***

Jack Plunkett's call to Colonel Karl Berenson put the blocking force in Jack's in-box when Karl said: "Get over here soonest."

Karl was somber, even depressed, an ominous sign from a man whose reputation for coolness and grace under pressure was legend. As they shook hands, Karl motioned without a word to a chair, and Jack seated himself. He had that feeling of being called to the principal's office knowing that he hadn't done anything to earn a prize. He could have reached out and touched the gloom that pervaded Karl's space.

"Jack, please just listen."

He was making an effort to control himself. Jack had never seen his friend so shaken. Not even on that first day as new cadets at West Point many summers ago when the whole system conspired to confuse them.

"Jack, SOG is being told to terminate border crossings upon receipt of a message outgoing as we speak."

He paused, and Jack, thinking Karl was finished, said:

"Sure. I don't have a detailed after action report yet, but what I have adds up to a 'mission accomplished.' Over 100 enemy trucks destroyed and some two to four hundred enemy KIA. We did what we set out to do. Their logistics system has been knocked for a loop. It's time to get our guys out. I'd do the same thing."

Karl stared at his old friend. The room was menacingly quiet for several beats before Karl broke the silence.

"Jack, I couldn't believe it either when I was told. You didn't register what I said. No more border crossings. No—more—border—crossings!"

Jack Plunkett was suddenly transfigured. He was a man in shock.

"God forgive me for even saying it! Do you mean we aren't going to recover our guys?"

Karl put his hands to his face as he looked at his old friend.

"I couldn't comprehend it when the National Security Adviser told me to do it. He had just come from the President. He told me to get a message to General Abrams immediately. Then he dictated the message. Here it is."

Karl reached for the plain spiral notebook on his desk and passed it to Jack. It was turned to a page with some hastily scribbled words in Karl's handwriting that doomed American soldiers who obeyed without question what duly appointed or elected civilian officials told them to do.

> *To: Gen. A*
> *Terminate all ops fm RVN into Laos and Camb as of rcpt this msg. Repeat: terminate cross border ops now. Do not cross into Laos. Repeat: Do not cross into Laos.*
> *Chmn JCS sends*

Jack let it all seep in. Then he spoke softly and slowly.

"Karl, for the sake of clarity, I say back for possible correction: my government intends to leave some 35 Americans and 140 of our CIDG in a denied area?"

"That's what the man said."

"And that message goes from the Chairman to Abe?"

"That's what the man said."

"Did your boss tell the Chairman?"

"I don't know. I don't think so."

"The rats are leaving the sinking ship. And the bastards take the Chairman's name in vain? Karl, what do you intend to do?"

"The first thing I did was to tell my boss to stick it in his ear. If he wants that message to go, he'll have to get another boy."

"I'm sure that's no problem in this town. I bet the message is on its way to Honolulu and Saigon right now."

"Sorry to say you're right. No shortage of people on the make and suck-ups."

"No reflection on you, Karl, but Machiavelli is in. Some of those SOBs absolutely revel in hardball. Call them heartless and they act like that's praise."

"You got that right. Call 'em gutless and they might strangle an old lady or a kitten to show how hard they are. Any old lady or kitten will do."

"Jack, the next thing I'm going to do is have a cup of coffee with you, my last of many in the White House. Then I'll pack my personal stuff and ask the Army what it plans to do with me. I can't stay here."

"There might be a Browning Automatic Rifle man out there who would take you as an assistant. Do you remember the immediate action drill if a BAR malfunctions?"

To Jack's amazement, without skipping a beat Karl responded:

"Pull, push, tap, aim, fire."

Jack raised his eyebrows as an image formed in his mind.

"Karl, can you imagine how Pietro will react to this?"

"No. How about Mark?"

"Jesus! If I were Counselor to the President, I'd put Mark in irons before he goes on a rampage."

CHAPTER FOURTEEN

End Game: On the Ground

Socked In

Day was one wet son of a bitch and had his hands full of tactical problems. Without knowing that his masters in Washington had sold him out, the dense rainclouds, thick ground fog, and sheets of water told him that he was in trouble. He was in deep kimchee, as he put it in 1953 when he was nineteen in Korea. And immortal.

He had just returned from trooping the line, counting noses, checking fighting positions, and generally bucking up his soggy troops. His effective strength was 34 U.S. Special Forces and 123 little people, mostly Montagnards. In addition to combat casualties and the mindless accident that killed a man in the first moments of the operation, sickness had taken a toll among the Montagnards. Few people outside of the Special Forces community knew that the Yards were 100% malarial, and 100% tubercular. Attrition to sickness usually began a few days into a combat operation as malaria flared into high fevers. The TB caused the victims to bark at night like so many dogs.

The poor bastards couldn't help it. They were game, but nature always won. The heavy rain and chilly weather ensured that everyone was sick. Only those who had lived in the Central Highlands realized how cold it could get in the tri-border area and in the mountains of Vietnam and Laos. The cold was intensified when a body was wet with rain and sweat for days.

Air support had been unavailable for the last six hours. No tac air. No gunships. No resupply. He had medevaced two very sick Montagnards and a U.S. NCO with a broken ankle on the last birds out of the bush. He wouldn't ask gutsy chopper pilots to deal with zero viz and enemy anti-air fires surely concentrating around the Americans. The choppers would come. They always came. But it was likely that they'd get lost in rain clouds and ground fog or plow into a mountain. He refused to risk their lives. Even if they found us, he speculated, landing was very dicey.

Ken Key approached his leader to cheer him up. Handing him a steaming cup of coffee, he said:

"Major, I always said that you are all wet. Now, just look at you. Have some of this before you spit shine those boots. Looks like you shined them with a Hershey bar."

Day took the cup in numb hands, sipping from it as he looked at his unidentifiable canvas and leather jungle boots, now two globs of red mud. They weighed one ton per foot. For an instant the image of Michael Mud, his first grader son, flashed in his mind. He touched his wallet with the photo of the boy, grinning and covered in mud as he played with a shovel after a Virginia rain. He was four years old in the picture taken when the Major Day was a captain on his first tour in Vietnam. The mud was the red clay layering God's earth from Virginia to Georgia. And in Vietnam. And in Laos. What's with red clay?

Immediacy jerked him back to Laos, 1970.

"I'll spit shine my boots right after I eat the fruit cheese cake you ordered from the downtown Konditorei. Please check the temperature of today's wine."

The banter conformed to the code of the old combat soldier—when it all turns to shit, ain't nuthin' to do but giggle. Bonding has an almost pejorative connotation in some circles and has become shopworn, but bonding, or something like it, is the glue of unit cohesion. The boys at Thermopylae and the Alamo, the Marines at Wake Island and on the Yalu River, the GIs at Bastogne, Fat Albert and his Yards, they all knew it. It was bad form to talk about it, except in bad films. Good form was to share a coffee and corny banter and jokes. The dumbest man in the blocking force knew that American air power was required here and now. The dumbest man also saw that it just wasn't going to happen. Only Covey was up there, way up there, making holes in the sky and acting as radio relay.

"Anything from Dak To?"

"Negative, sir. Kontum reports weather unchanged for the next 24 hours."

"Umm. Nothing but good news today. Next you'll tell me the Red Sox beat the Yankees. Anything from our outposts?"

"Negative."

Limited visibility forced unpleasant decisions. To prevent the enemy from surprising and overrunning the blocking position in a short bound with a large force, Day put OPs in front of the friendly positions. Miserable and vulnerable two man OPs were changed every hour to keep them alert and to allow them to dry out, warm up, and rest. Their job was to provide early warning, to give the main body a few minutes to clear the cobwebs, man all fighting positions, and to get crew served weapons—machine guns, recoilless rifles, and mortars—up and ready to fire final protective lines, if necessary. That would put interlocking fires in front of the defenders for as long as ammunition lasted.

***

The battle for the blocking position began minutes after Day's inquiry, as though on cue. Report of the exchange of fire in front of his location was passed to Dak To and simultaneously picked up by Kontum and Covey. Dak To and Kontum gave a "Roger." Covey flew to the vicinity of the blocking force and continued to monitor radio communications and to relay as required.

Carpenter and the pilot looked down from an altitude they believed to be just above the trees. They saw a blur of gray on gray. At absolute minimum altitude—risking an abrupt meeting with a mountain or a tree—the grayness became an impenetrable, opaque, elongated marshmallow pressed to the earth. Hoping to see flashes marking the firefight, they were disappointed. Pilot and observer conferred and confirmed that neither saw a hint of human activity below.

"Highwire, this is Covey. I'm directly over you. Can't see shit."

Unsurprised, Day responded:

"Roger."

"I'll loiter."

"Roger."

The command group at Dak To monitored the exchange but, to their credit, remained silent. Day didn't need advice. He needed tactical air. There was none. No viz, no air.

Talk from OPs to the main body of the blocking force was minimal. The dialogue of automatic weapons told the story. CAR-15s spoke and AK-47s responded. That was the early warning. The OPs had executed their early warning missions. Their next stunt was to get back in one piece to the main body and to become a part of the defense. If they could.

The command group heard the sustained fire of a pair of M-60s alternating short bursts of fire; then another OP contact; then another pair of M-60s; then a third pair of M-60s. Then the distinctive thunk of the M-79, the 40mm grenade launcher that joined the chorus of M-16s, machine guns, and the boom of Claymore mines.

"Major, I'm kinda glad you loaded up with machine guns," said Ken Key.

"Trust me, Uncle Ken. You are in the hands of a master, and the evil foe is in the clutches of a demented demon."

The radio operators surrounding the Mad Major and Key in the bunker heard every word of this exchange, looked at one another, and finally broke into loud laughter and guffaws when one of them sang, off key:

"Jesus loves me, this I know, cuz the Bible tells me so."

Another picked up the beat, intoning:

"Life is just a bowl of cherries...."

Not to be outdone by the riffraff, the Major, in a simulation of the basso profundo voice and mock-heroic intonation—in the manner of "Time Marches On" propaganda at the movies during WWII—said: *"De oppresso liber."*

One of the NCOs, no doubt an older mackerel-snapper brought up in the Latin Mass and Gregorian chant, gave it a long "amen" that revealed the Southie in his Latin. The Major scrupulously avoided the appropriate response that came to mind: Ite Missa est, the penultimate words of the Mass spoken by a priest: the Mass is ended. But he vocalized the last words, the response, *Deo gratias.* That's for the laity. Thanks be to God.

***

The radio came to life. A platoon leader in contact with the enemy requested his pre-registered mortar concentration. It was effective. The volume and tone of his voice indicated glee:

"Repeat! Repeat! It's right on them!"

As the major looked in the general direction of OP 1, where the C-130 gunship had killed so many enemy, his ears said that this time the enemy assault was coming from his left rear, from 6 to 9 o'clock. His fighters had it under control. No need to shift troops or to commit his puny reserve of one squad. He wished he had a full platoon in reserve, but if wishes were wings, we could all fly to Kontum. He needed his 360-degree perimeter manned. No telling the direction of the next assault. He also needed the machine guns, 57s, and mortars manned. No way to cover 360 degrees and have a bigger reserve, even when he had all his people. If it got sticky, he'd move his entire force to the prepared alternate positions up the hill a bit, thereby reducing the size of the perimeter. The airlifted bulldozers had made that option possible. The smaller perimeter higher up would require fewer troops. But not yet. Later, when things got sticky. Tactics, like love making, was all about timing. Bleed the enemy. He's exposed. We have good cover. Continue the mission.

Day gave Radich status reports out of habit, thinking: "Keep the boss informed so he and his high-priced help can think about what they might do for me. The boss knows what I want; it's the only thing I can't have: air support. Go with what I got. Keep Dak To informed. When the weather breaks, air assets are my security blanket. Meanwhile, pour fire on enemy troops in the open. Can't be too much fun for them, rolling in mud under heavy fire after a long forced march and thinking about death from the sky."

The firing diminished, becoming silence in the 6 to 9 o'clock direction. It was more than a probe. The platoon leader reported enemy bodies stacked in the wire. The machine guns, mines, and mortars had taken a toll of brave infantry soldiers who were now enemy dead.

Then he heard an encore at his 3 o'clock. OP small arms action and the thud of grenades warned the defenders that trouble was brewing to the east. Machine gun and mortar fires were to his right front.

The platoon leader facing 6 to 9 reported one friendly KIA and six WIA. All outposts were in. He estimated some thirty enemy KIA or WIA. He had a POW, a wounded NVA soldier. His unit was the 66th Regiment. Says many of his friends killed and wounded. Says another NVA regiment has joined the battle.

Barely digesting the status report and passing it to Dak To, Day heard heavy fire from 3 o'clock and 9 o'clock and the sound of motors at 12 o'clock. The hill was lighting up like a pinball machine. The OP 1 at 12 o'clock reported the sound of motors as suspected enemy tanks were moving toward him. He estimated four or five motors, probably PT-76s. Range, about 400 meters from the friendly main body.

That would be in the direction of the initial contacts. Map study and earlier patrols in that direction confirmed that this was the most likely avenue of approach for armor. No doubt the enemy commander would like to surprise the American, but terrain severely restricted his options. If he wanted to use armor to shock and roll over his enemy, he'd have to attack from the defender's 12 o'clock. There's too much thick vegetation everywhere else. Good! As they teach at Fort Benning, the enemy is now canalized. The only way to improve on that, he thought, was for the bad guys to get homesick.

Anticipating attack from the north, Day had plotted mortar

concentrations along the most probable avenue of attack. In close to the barbed wire was a pre-registered barrage. Air would be most desirable at this moment, but the defenders would rely upon their own 81mm mortars and the 57mm surprise he had in store for the NVA tankers. They won't find point targets until they themselves become targets. They expect to shock us. Wrong! I think they're in mobile coffins.

***

"All High Wire stations, this is 6."

"This is One, over."

"Two."

"Three."

"Mortars."

"This is Six. Get on Lima Lima now. Use that means to me and to mortars as long as it's in."

When things got hot and heavy, radios would be crowded with emergency transmissions, so they used telephones. When they were moving about, that wouldn't be possible. And he knew wires would be cut. Until then, he wanted to clear the radio command frequency of less urgent messages. As soon as the shit hits the fan, everyone wants to talk on the radio. Happens every time. No hard-core soldier would confess to nervousness. Folks just want to know that somebody out there loves 'em. But commo discipline makes for a tidy battlefield.

He alerted the leaders to possible tanks in the general direction of 12 o'clock and reminded them of the game plan.

"OK. Tell your 57mm gunners we want to surprise the tanks. All platoon leaders control those weapons. Nobody pops until High Wire One fires. He'll see them first to his front. When he estimates all tanks are in sight, he executes. Then pile on! I don't want any to get away. Questions?"

He got what he expected from his guys:

"One. Negative."

"Two. Negative."

"Three. Negative."

"Mortars. Negative."

"Good. Clean their clocks. I estimate that One also will make best use of mortars. One, you put mortars on 'em first—early. I want them worried about the mortars all the way. I want them buttoned up. Then, when you think he's put all his tanks out there mutually supporting, you initiate the 57s. Got it?"

"Rog, Six. Harass him with 81s all the way. Put 57s on him when all tanks in sight."

And it was done.

The PT-76s charged full of oats. They were the biggest dudes in the 'hood. As they passed through the mortar concentrations buttoned up in the shitty weather, they probably felt confident and snug going up against light infantry. NVA rockets and mortars pounded the hill in support of five tanks. Behind the tanks two companies of infantry trailed in line.

But it became a turkey shoot. Few enemy tanks even spotted a target. Only one fired its main gun.

Because of the poor visibility, the tanks were suddenly there, shadowy forms fifty meters away and closing, right in a barrage of 81mm mortars. The leader of the first platoon tapped the 57 gunner next to him. The first tank burped, bumped, and stopped. The gunner moved under cover to his alternate firing position as four more 57s fired within seconds. There was no missing at this range. With his second shot he hit a second PT-76. The machine guns took on the infantry following closely on the heels of the tanks. Mortars and machine guns chewed up infantry and tankers who bailed out of tanks. No one got out of the two tanks in flames. M-79s, CAR-15s, and M-16s added their fire. The 57s put round after round into the tanks and infantry.

Enemy troops withdrew into the rain and ground fog; enemy rocket and mortar fire ceased; the battlefield was quiet. Day ordered a police of the battlefield. Patrols brought back over a hundred weapons, a dozen wounded enemy troops, and two unmarked POWs dazed and in a state of shock. The victory had been gained with the loss of one American life and five wounded Montagnards, two seriously. All friendly casualties were caused by direct hits on fighting positions.

Day met with his leaders to pass on his estimate of the situation.

The enemy had no choice. He had to root the American blocking force out of his main line of communication. He had to take advantage of the weather currently denying the Americans support from the air. The best solution to the enemy's problem was to attack at night. Soon. Therefore, Day said:

"Ya done good. Redistribute ammunition; get some food in your troops; get combat ineffectives to the medical bunker; get destroyed commo wire, Claymores, and barbed wire back in. Mortars, get illumination rounds for the 81s ready. Everybody on 50% alert until further notice."

He looked at the circle of faces watching him. They knew the score. He wanted to hug them, but he used his bland professional voice:

"Our success so far comes out of anticipating. This is the night of the machine gun."

Ken Key spoke for the first time.

"Sir, may I add something?"

"Sure."

"PS: Pray for good weather."

There were "amens," "rogers," "right ons" and one "fuckin' A."

***

Feelings of pride and concern were conflated in Dak To, Kontum, Saigon, Honolulu, and Washington among those tracking events on the Ho Chi Minh trail. Results exceeded pre-mission expectations. Ridgerunner, Robbie, Joe, and Day had thus far used skills and cool courage to bleed the enemy badly. The stay-behinds at CCC and the support folks at Dak To were glued to the radios. They sang songs of praise to their buddies, but they knew that without air support the NVA would put on a full court press. Enemy soldiers would die, but the enemy troops in this neighborhood had shown again and again, since 1965, that they were very good at dying—and fighting. CCC would pay a high price.

Pietro, Radich, and Burns were numb from emotional and intellectual overload. They shared pride in the skill of their men in Laos, but the weather that isolated the blocking force and prevented its extraction profoundly worried the leaders. Ordered not to cross the border! They could not believe the order. When it was confirmed, they were enraged. Then they learned the meaning of despair.

The three old soldiers monitoring the launch site radio had functioned at both ends of the operational umbilical cord. They had been at risk at the cutting edge, completely dependent upon soldiers into whose hands each of them had put his life, more than once. And they had held the lives of others in their own hands. Often. The enemy, the elements, God, error, radio failure, dumb luck, friendly fire, stupidity, Fate—any of these could kill. Old soldiers know these things. But it had never entered their minds that their leaders in Washington would give away American lives. American soldiers don't desert American soldiers. Period. No matter if the task were near impossible, the intent always was to execute the mission and care for the men. Always. American soldiers were secure in the knowledge that their nation, commanders, and friends would make extraordinary efforts to rescue them. Always. Now the three old soldiers in the Dak To bunker believed they were a party to betrayal. Talking about it couldn't fix it, but they needed to talk about it. They did.

In fact, the betrayal in Washington had no immediate effect on the blocking force. It was ironic. The wretched weather in the Central Highlands prohibited air support, reinforcement, and extraction. But the intent of the words out of the White House hurt.

***

A message from Laos broke the rushing sound of one of the radios. They all recognized the Day's voice.

"Circus Six, this is High Wire Six, over."

Radich took the handset from the commo man.

"Circus Six, over."

"SITREP. We've been taking rockets and mortars for the last five minutes. Still zero visibility. Expect assault any time."

Radich for the moment couldn't think of a thing to say. He certainly was not going to tell a dead man that his government had decided not to lift a finger to help him. Day knew as well as Radich that weather socked in Laos, Pleiku, Kontum, and Dak To. He would not expect air support of any kind. That had been topic number one on the radio since the weather turned bad. Not realizing that the Major had thought the same thing of his subordinates just minutes earlier, Radich thought: He's a big boy. He knows the score.

Seconds had passed. It just felt like a long time.

"Roger. How are your bunkers and overhead cover holding up?"

That sounded relevant, but Radich thought how much like a Sunday telephone call to his mother it was. Once the latest news was exchanged, the chat wound down.

But what else? What's to say? How are the wife and kids? This is your chance for fame and immortality? Get some of those dirty rats for me?

The experienced soldiers knew that in minutes or hours it would be over. They weren't going to begin bullshitting the troops at this late stage of their Service together.

Day's report answered Radich's question directly.

"Overhead and bunkers outstanding. We little piggies built a house of brick. The other guy doesn't even have a house of straw. Poor bastard is wet and mucking about in red slops. No hot showers waiting for him. When he gets here he gets dead."

"Roger."

"It takes direct hits to hurt us. We've had two of those. I'm popping illum with 81s. I'm glad I loaded up with beau coup M-60s."

"Great show earlier! Gotcha some tanks."

"Rog. Turkey shoot. The tanks came fat and sassy. We jumped them with 57s. Got 'em all. Then our machine guns and mortars waxed troops in the open."

"Well done. The S-4 has something."

"Gotta be fast. Some probing. Over."

"Leprechaun here. Message from Mr. Jameson: Take care of business and get back for a bit of the dog that bit you!"

"Wilco, Mac. Love to. Got business. Out."

He handed the handset to the commo man, grabbed his weapon, and moved to the sound of the guns.

CHAPTER FIFTEEN

Las Vegas, The Gathering

Another Flight

Roger Pietro turned from the aircraft window to glance at his Special Operations Association membership card. He was a lifetime member and one of the founders. On the front of the card were his name, membership number, and the SOA logo: a Green Beret on a death's head, wings above the skull, anchor below. On the back of the card were the words: "You have never lived until you have almost died. Life has a special meaning that the protected will never know." At thirty thousand feet his mind drifted between the then and the now in sweet-sad reverie.

His solitary trip from Washington was self-imposed. He could have had the company of others on the flight to Las Vegas. At least half dozen men from the Washington Chapter would attend the annual reunion, and he was a beloved old soldier. He knew that. He was modest about it, but he was very proud that the NCOs and junior officers of 1970 held him in high regard, even affection. But there would be time for mingling, embracing, and talking later, at the reunion. For now, sky gazing, reading, Martinis, and remembering felt just right. Did the Martinis make it so? They helped. So did solitude and reflection. He saw the sky out there as an unwritten page, awaiting inscription from his memory. OK, he mused smiling, and from the Martinis. But more than anything else, it's the men he knew in thirty years of soldiering. It's been another thirty years since Major Day's blocking force in Laos was overrun. It took months for the NVA to restore their lines of communication in the tri-border area and to resupply their forces in Vietnam south of Kontum. Mission accomplished. Can't claim victory. We didn't do victory anymore. Our mission was accomplished. Then the force was overrun in the rain. Did it matter?

The war limped along for another five years before Saigon became Ho Chi Minh City. NVA tanks were at the President's Palace. Crowds scrambled in the streets, at the Embassy and at the airport. Grab ass as choppers took off from city roofs. Ugly sights on TV produced bad memories as we deserted Viet and Montagnard friends.

Pietro mused: "At the highlight and conclusion of the reunion, the banquet, we'll recall the good men. Overrun. Do we celebrate overrun? Nah. We celebrated VE Day and VJ Day as victories. Old fashioned. Now we commemorate. Like kissing your sister. That's it. Since 1953 in Korea, that's what we do: commemorate non-wars. No declaration of war, no peace treaty. When an antithetical system collapses from its corruption and internal contradictions, we credit our capitalism and democracy. But I'll save geopolitics for another day with smartasses in Washington. I'm here to remember with friends. Preserve the memory. Honor the good memories of good men.

"God, do I remember. I see them as they were, and I see them at reunions. The babies are now 55. Most are sixty, seventy. Old men. How the hell did that happen? They pop into my head as cocky studs in jungle fatigues, packing CAR-15s or AKs or Swedish Ks and ready for anything. And the ones I don't see at reunions are eternally fit, brown, gung-ho rascals, fixed forever like figures on a Grecian urn. Joe Waldon, Robbie, Major Day and others remain forever in memory the way they looked the day they were inserted into Laos, onto the trail.

Ridgerunner and Mike Schaefer made it. Ridgerunner's not a reunion kind of guy. He never showed a sense of loss when his people were killed, so why would he pretend to care now? He'd say it was a doing thing, and it's done. There was purpose then, now it's over. Move on. He's a special case, detached, a quiet loner, a very hard man.

"There were other hard men. Some were technicians of violence, craftsmen of great skill. Some were romantics and didn't know it. Volunteers. All of them lived on the edge where a slip could be fatal. And they liked it. Maybe they needed that the way a druggie needs a hit. Were we war lovers or idealists? Dunno. Were there crazies among us? Probably. Most likely we would have been Freikorps irregulars in 1920; Reds or Whites in Russia; Germanien howling with "a silly passion for war" as they emerged from dark forests to fight and defeat Roman soldiers about the time of Christ.

"Mike Schaefer will come to his first reunion. He's a big time lawyer. No, he's still 25 years old and the RT One-Zero, at least in my mind's eye. Over 55? Hell, 60! Why not? Cripes, I've been retired about 30 years.

"Never thought I'd forget any of the names, but now I have some faces without names and names without faces. Sic transit gloria mundi. Some of the lost souls, who show up for the first time, or after a long absence, are easily recognizable. Some aren't. Sometimes I recognize a guy right away and the name won't come. Sometimes the name is right there. Don't think of some guy for over twenty years and his name is right on the tip of my tongue when I lay eyes on him.

"Of course I can see Mark Burns and Radich—why was he always Radich? Burns was Mark; I was P or Roger to them and probably "the colonel" to the RT men. Ridgerunner was always Ridgerunner. Another martini will help me puzzle that all out. Better than a shrink.

"A dry one. Two olives, please, the ones with the answers."

***

"I see Radich at my elbow in the CCC launch site bunker in Dak To, so many years ago. Feels like yesterday. Worst weather the Central Highlands had ever seen. And that's a mouthful. Had God wanted to give the world an enema, He'd stick the hose in the tri-border area. Maybe in Dak To. In that bunker.

"I had known Radich for a lot of years before that. He was about 45. Got picked up for colonel just about then. Thanks for bloody campaigns and sickly seasons, as the Brits say. Good for promotions. I'll recognize him right away. He was too much the Far East rat. His wife got tired of him extending tours in Vietnam and serving other tours in Thailand and Formosa without her. Was he a big cock hound? Don't remember. Don't think so. I think it was just that he liked soldiers and the Far East more than he liked white picket fences, the PTA, backyard cookouts, and the Little League. She divorced him. Can't blame her. He liked us more than he liked her. And she knew it. So did Kipling.

"Mark became famous, not for victories but for a highly publicized rescue failure some years later. Nah. Not fair. He did command Project Delta. He was never my cup of tea, but how can a professional soldier bad-mouth a man whose only ambition was to die for his country while earning the Medal of Honor? Retired a colonel without The Medal. Without a star. Not many stars among the old true believers. Then Mark dies in bed. In peacetime. Bet that pissed him off.

"Jack Plunkett said he'd be here. He was the best of us. Should have gotten lots of stars. Should have been the Army Chief of Staff or Chairman of the JCS. Great soldier. Troops loved him. And smooth as goose shit in dealing with the slick pols and smart civilians in the White House, DOD, CIA, and State. Retired a colonel after 30 years. Did some college teaching before he became a guide for Outward Bound. Beats drinking too much and telling war stories to old guys at the VFW.

"Karl took it hardest of all. Left the White House and shot himself. The bastards said the suicide was caused by the pressure, overwork, that he couldn't handle the heat at the top. Bullshit. He overdosed on honor and decency. He was too good for the pricks. Too good for this world.

"PJ Riley was a hotshot newspaper guy in Boston. Made his rep as a kid reporter in Vietnam and certified it in Baghdad twenty years later, after stops in Cyprus, Central America—wherever young men were killing one another and bystanders. He also reported official school bussing and recreational killing in the Combat Zone in Boston; religious crazies and mass suicide in Jonestown; child molesters, killers, drugs, slums; Russians in Afghanistan. Have typewriter, will travel. Apparently only Pulitzer or canonization remains. Or a best seller. He's seen a lot of wars. Knows all the wordsmiths and editors, Cronkite, Safer and those Young Turks MACV officials loved to hate: Halberstam, Sheehan, Arnett. They wrote their books and became talking heads on TV. Shouldn't hold PJ's success against him, but he hurt us. Couldn't wait with his big story. Turns out he spooked the politicians into a gutless move. Was that his fault? Probably.

"Think happy thoughts at 30,000 feet. The Leprechaun, Mac, will be there. Replaced Day as the director of operations and intelligence in CCC when Day was killed. Troops loved him. Not everyone could manage those wild men. Radich could. Mac could. Day could. Mike Schaefer called Day the leader of the Spike Jones Band. Good way to describe that Kontum gang. Or SOG. CCC guys were to the Army as Spike Jones was to music. I guess we were."

But deliberate focus on some happy memories couldn't hold off his strongest feelings that dwarfed all others. His smile was rueful. What he saw as he looked into the aircraft window was Fat Albert carrying a wounded Montagnard and directing his One-One to get the team to an extraction point. Should have that as a bronze statue near the Reflecting Pool, not far from the Vietnam Memorial. Fat chance. The old soldier couldn't think of a better way to die, but America would never hear of Fat Albert.

He chewed the second olive.

Parody of Paradise

Well before the final approach, the Las Vegas airport was visible as a glow at twelve o'clock: of course. There's nothing else here. The city is a lit match in a large dark room.

Pietro hated everything about the place. But the guys like it. Gambling profits make meals, drinks, rooms, and entertainment cheap. Daytime temperatures soared above 100 degrees as one strolled around outside to escape the confinement of the hotel, encountering pathetic souls from purgatory, limping uncomfortably from casino to casino with plastic containers filled with coins for the one-armed bandits. The eyes of these people were dead. What an awful place. And hot.

The wheels didn't fall off upon landing. His bag made it. The cabbie, a retired soldier, found the Plaza. As Pietro entered the hotel, he looked up to check the underside of the marquee. Yes, he remembered right. It was still an Olympic champion in tastelessness, consisting of bare incandescent light bulbs spaced four inches apart covering what seemed to be an acre of overhead. It was a parody. Of what? Elegance? Versailles? Some poor soul did tasteless and saw elegance. Guess that's what tasteless means.

All of this noted, not for the first time, and filed.

He checked in and found himself armed with a plastic card that served as a room key. High-tech is everywhere. Noting the location of the hospitality suite, he proceeded first to his room. He had to go through the casino, whatever one's destination. No option. The damned place looked the same at midnight, 8 p.m., or 8 a.m. There was no reference to anything outside. Food, drink, and restrooms were readily available. Get 'em in and keep 'em in the gambling rooms. Beats being a POW. Not by much. Hard as hell to find an exit. Easy to find a machine ready to take a coin, any coin, penny or silver dollar. Or a card. The pews of one-armed bandits for the hopeful faithless stretched to eternity.

Tired-looking employees in the casino were cartoon versions of female beauty drawn by Walt Disney or Famous Studios animators. Some women were has-beens, but most never were. They showed lots of bosom and thigh north of chunky legs in see-through black mesh stockings. Faces painted in bold colors reached for beauty and achieved grotesqueness. The package was topped with hair more appropriate to a window display mannequin than to someone's mother, wife, or sister. Carrying trays of drinks to gamblers beat working eight-or ten-hour shifts at checkout station in a food store. Come to think of it, there are more casinos than food stores in this town.

Arriving at the door to his room, he cursed as he tried the card that never opened the door to his room with his first try. Must be the card's fault.

He recalled the chatter of the master of ceremonies in Cabaret. He needed three languages to capture the decadence of Berlin on the eve of the Nazi take-over. Las Vegas does it with one language.

And no music.

Progress.

The American way.

So, he asked himself, why does the curmudgeon subject himself to tasteless things and pitiable people in a city that makes him uncomfortable? For the same reason you tolerated careerist senior officers, cold coffee, wet toilet paper, ambitious politicos, and spoiled civilians not good enough to lick the dust from Fat Albert's jump boots. For over 30 years it was the men, asshole. It's still the men.

After two or three tries, the plastic card or the Holy Spirit opened the door to his room. It failed Opulence 101, but it had a bed and a shower. He sat on the bed to ruminate.

Pietro, Mike, and PJ

Most members of the Special Operations Association are Special Forces Vietnam veterans. Army and Air Force aviators—chopper pilots, Covey pilots, gunship pilots, and Blackbird pilots—are members. Some U.S. Navy. But mostly SF. Some World War II, Korea, Grenada, and Panama. Some Desert Storm/Desert Shield, Somalia, and secret Cold War dust-ups. But most are Vietnam vets, mostly SOG men.

Some had served a few years and gotten on with their lives. Others were professional soldiers who had worn the uniform for 20 to 30 years. It was always a source of pride for Pietro to note how many of the old guys had done well. They retired as Sergeant Major, First Sergeant, Colonel, and Lieutenant Colonel. Several were middle grade NCOs when he met them and majors and captains when they ended their Service—always upper case "S" for Service in Pietro's lexicon. The survivors had done well. We even have a few Generals, real soldiers who were surprised to end their careers wearing stars. They had their great adventures and satisfaction in SF and the good sense to command good conventional outfits.

The KIAs had also done well.

At the inaugural luncheon Pietro spotted and greeted a suspected Mike Schaefer. A check of the nametag confirmed that the bearer was guilty as charged. It was, indeed, the RT Montana One-Zero. The Leprechaun was there, and so were Radich, Ken Key, and the lieutenant who survived the final assault on the blocking position. What was his name? Schell. Pete Schell. Good soldier. And Jack Plunkett showed up.

Pietro greeted familiar faces and new ones. The NCOs and junior officers who did the heavy lifting back then admired him. They knew he had worried about them constantly. He tracked each RT each day it was deployed "over the fence," sweating out their crises and cheering their triumphs. They were not anonymous "troops." By the way he greeted them in safe places, they knew that he knew them by face, name and reputation. In retirement, his and theirs, he regularly took calls from his "boys." They gave him updates, SITREPS, status reports, problems, successes, dreams, weddings, births and graduations. Increasingly the reports were of divorce, illness and death, a sure sign that Someone is flipping the pages of the calendar. But there was also news of children promoted to senior sergeant and lieutenant colonel, usually in Special Forces, and of advances in civilian careers. Several of Pietro's lieutenants from those days are retired colonels. Hell, some sons of friends are colonels and sergeants major. A couple of grandchildren are serving as sergeants and lieutenants.

Sometimes the call came from a man with a pistol in his hand and suicide on his mind, wanting to talk. Pietro had their trust then and now. He always had time to listen.

Meeting Mike Schaefer for the first time since Vietnam days was special, and Pietro said so. Both felt a permanent bond.

"Mike, you peel away a lot of years. We missed you. You belong here. I'd hate to think that any of our guys believe that this is an association of lifers."

"Sir, I can't say why I didn't come earlier: school, career, family, the usual excuses for not doing something. And I didn't know about the association and reunions until recently. It's been a jolt to see these guys. I didn't think I could care so much. I keep looking for the Major, Robbie, Joe...."

"Yes. Just the way you say it. But it's Roger. Please call me Roger."

"No, sir. I'm not subject to the Uniform Code of Military Justice. You will always be 'the Colonel,' and Major Day is 'the Major.' It's just the way it is."

"Funny. I was just thinking how we addressed one another back then. You were Montana. Now you are counselor."

"No, that's my cover. I'm proud to be Montana."

"I'd be proud to be Montana."

Pietro meant exactly that. An old professional soldier saw the men who led Montana, California, Arizona, New York, Delaware, Alaska, and the others as the essence of what it means to be a soldier. They were also legend to later special operators.

"What was it like for you after CCC and the Army, Mike? Did you fit in? What did you make of it all back in the very troubled U.S. of that time ?"

"You still do a rigorous debrief, Colonel, a cross examination, in my current line of work."

Schaefer paused. He looked back over thirty years, trying to get it right, thinking, "How do we get it right? Did I think a certain way then, or is the now-me projecting the then-me?" He knew his current version of the truth. There are other versions. Truth is a slippery devil. Words seemed inadequate to the task.

"I didn't try to fit in."

"In the neighborhood, my friends were mostly blue collar, like me, guys who served in the 173rd, 101st, the Cav, Marine Corps, LRRPs as some kind of grunt. After law school, most of my old pals were in construction trades, or cops and firefighters. Some were teachers. Then, I had professional colleagues who became friends. It was ten years after law school before I mixed them. I can't say why. At some point, that seemed the right thing to do. Until then I drank beer and played ball with neighborhood buddies. I did my job and enjoyed the company of professionals. Few of the professional people were vets, and few of the neighborhood guys weren't. I didn't think about, it at the time, but I guess I lived in two subcultures."

Pietro had thought that issue through, the difference between the pros and the Christmas help when the war was over and life went on.

"It was easier for us, Mike. We soldiers were constantly with kindred souls. In training, in the bar, mess hall, PX, professional schools or in a cafeteria visiting one another. Drinking buddies were my working buddies, all Vietnam vets. We didn't have to change masks. My friends were soldiers. And we met one another around the world—Bragg, Okie, Germany—the SF subculture."

Mike reflected for a moment.

"I hadn't thought about it, but that's right. Career men had less social tension than those of us who returned to civilian life. You didn't have to assess the people around you before you expressed views. In peacetime you trained. In crunch time you went to Saudi, Panama, Somalia, Bosnia. You had one another at Bragg, Bad Toelz, Okie, Devens. Even in the Pentagon. Different places but the same guys."

"Right. I didn't accept all the stories of screwed up Vietnam vets. My friends are veterans of hard combat, almost all of them. Few are screwed up. Now two ideas pop into my head. One, we were a mutual support group and didn't much think about it. It's true. We always had one another. Two, we had our drunks and weirdoes, but we just didn't connect their behavior to combat. They were just some of our odd balls, more comic relief than psycho cases deserving pity. The PTSD stuff came later. It makes sense now. At the time, we thought that was civilian talk, pussy excuses. Chaplains, medics and good commanders managed that stuff by punching your Tough Shit Card."

Pietro and Mike talked for a long time as others joined them, pleased at delayed recognition of young men disguised as sixty year olds.

Pietro felt an urge to get the whole blocking force story on the table. We're dying out. I'm one of the few who knows the whole story. We should share our approximation of the truth before we die. A refrain from the past flitted through some part of his brain. He recited his recollection of it aloud for Mike's benefit:

And I always hear
Time's wing'ed chariot hurrying near.

Mike nodded. We get old, fail to notice, and then act as though our personal aging is unique in the history of man when we notice changes in the mirror as we brush our teeth or feel aches in joints and muscles for no apparent reason. Like we discovered it. GB Shaw said it right: Youth was wasted on the young. We geezers know that. Mike had a bit of news for his old boss: reference to a voice from a shared past.

"Colonel, you might be interested in a recent contact I had with PJ Riley. Remember him?"

"Yes. How could I forget? I'm very interested in your take on his behavior then. And what he thinks of it now."

And then, they realized that as long as they were in the hospitality room where it was very loud, interruptions were unavoidable.

"Mike, let's get out of here. We need a quiet place."

Pietro valued the happy reunions so important to men who once shared the most intense experiences of their lives. But he needed a talk with a smart and engaged man whose opinion of PJ—thirty years ago and now—mattered.

***

They walked across the street from the Plaza Hotel and found a quiet bar in the Golden Nugget Hotel, a rare oasis of privacy amidst gaming bustle. They ordered drinks.

"Tell me about Riley, Mike."

"Right. He called in 1980. In Chicago on assignment, he found me. We met, like now, two guys in a bar sharing memories.

"I'd seen his byline. He was in Vietnam at the end in Saigon and then in the Pentagon. I wasn't surprised. He was smart, quick on his feet, pair of balls, ambitious, personable.

"It was awkward: 1970 wasn't 1980. Back then, he did his job, I did mine.

"Maybe I lack moral courage, but I didn't want a pissing contest. He had the decency to call me. I think he was wrong not to wait with his story. He's ambivalent about that, but I know he was honestly angry that our government lied about ops over the fence. That's still on his mind. He believes that somebody has to watch the guys with the guns: cops and soldiers.

"He updated me on what he was doing, and I did the same about my career as a recently minted lawyer. Our parting was uncomfortable, but not acrimonious. There were several phone calls in ten years or so, and then silence. I somehow knew that he wound up as the foreign editor of the Boston Globe, that he had a retreat in Maine that he loved, and that he wrote a couple of books that were published. He seemed satisfied with his personal life and gratified by his professional success. And he lives in the right place. Bostonians are sure that they reside in Athens West, the capital of the Red Sox Nation, Harvard and all that.

"Then quiet. Until yesterday."

"He contacted you here"

"He called. Then he sent a FAX."

"Nothing for years, and then a FAX."

"Yeah. And what a FAX!"

Mike passed papers to Pietro who put on his neat rimless glasses. He began reading. Mike watched.

Mike,

After a dozen years of silence, I once more crash a SOG party to wish you and our friends well. I stumbled on the Special Operations Association Reunion—SOAR, an appropriate acronym—quite by accident. I guessed that the recon men would be there. The date got my antenna up. My observations in the attachment are for your eyes and for the old soldiers there, if you want to share them.

Covering the Balkans and Somalia took me back to our time in Vietnam. Indeterminacy and ambivalence cloud policies and events separated by decades. I don't believe you were wrestling with those demons at the time. You were engaged in the nitty gritty of combat and what needed to be done on the ground in real time. I thought it was wrong for the government of the people to lie to the people. Understand, I'm not inviting a debate. I am confessing to two convictions that share the same space: you and the recon men of 1970 were the finest soldiers I met in my career; I can't forgive our government for its deception of the American people.

Attached is the piece that will appear under my by-line in the

next Sunday opinion section of the Globe.
　　With respect,
　　PJ

Pietro glanced up, sipped his drink, and returned to PJ's copy.

Thirty years ago...

This reporter began his career covering war. We continue to debate the proper use of military force as the veterans of a long forgotten mission meet today. This is my tribute to the MACVSOG recon men and their successors around the world as we climb into our beds at night, snug and secure.

Special operations soldiers in 1970 died in the mud in the midst of torrential rains and a fierce hand-to-hand battle in Laos in a secret war as our country turned against the war in Vietnam. Those soldiers established the standards of skill and courage maintained by special operators today. Their legacy is treasured and cultivated.

In my work I meet young soldiers who continue to tell the stories of Robbie, Waldron, and Fat Albert. They aspire to measure up to the men meeting in Las Vegas now.

Somehow our indulgent society continues to produce men prepared to risk their lives for their friends and for the United States.

Our government must be judicious in the use of the extraordinary tool at its disposal: the men. Woe to the leader who misuses them, and damned be that leader who breaks faith with them.

To the recon men, old and new, and to special operators in places we don't know about—respect.

　　De oppresso liber
　　PJ Riley

Pietro returned the papers to Mike.

"He hasn't budged. He admires men like you, and trusts our government about as far as he can throw it."

"His copy will run in the Sunday edition of a major American newspaper."

"He blackmailed Radich. Said he'd hold the story if Radich would brief him on all aspects of a secret mission."

"True. But let me make the case for the defendant: 'Classified' meant nothing to him. And everything was new: Vietnam, Army jargon and rules, combat, figuring out what it was to be a journalist and an American, how to beat the competition and get past the Five O'Clock Follies to the truth. His education and his generation told him to question everything. The individual had to challenge 'the establishment.' Let's not forget how superheated politics were in the U.S. when we were in Vietnam. We had Tet '68 in Vietnam; the U.S. had assassinations and a kind of Tet in Chicago in 1968, and massive protests in Washington. PJ had all that 'question authority' baggage when he arrived in Vietnam. We had loyalty and the team and rules, like classified information. He was looking for a win. We broke rules by going over the fence. A sneak punch was within the non-rules of the game. For him and for us."

"You're too easy on him, too forgiving. He can 'fess up now and have it both ways: write a nice letter to feel good; be rich and famous."

"He honors special operators."

"After killing them. Words are cheap."

Mike just nodded. Loyalty mattered very much to him, but his analysis of international politics had evolved in the last three decades. Dominos didn't fall after South Vietnam fell. The Saigon government was never able to benefit its people or stand up to Hanoi. The Soviet Union collapsed due to inherent gross defects. He didn't like the ever-increasing selfishness and me-ism in his society, but that is not to say that our Vietnam policy in the 1960s was either correct or honest. Maybe we were played for suckers. But all of that was for another day, certainly not for a reunion of friends who had routinely risked their lives for their friends.

***

Later, upon returning to the hospitality room, Pietro was recognized by far more men than he recognized. Everyone knows the boss. Men he had met once or twice a long time ago remembered him. It took some little white lies when a smiling old guy presented his son as though Pietro was an intimate in the old days. Of course he confirmed the intimacy. Is there a greater honor than a man eagerly presenting his son to you? White lies are social cement. Even the Baltimore Catechism and the Sisters of Notre Dame would give him that.

Watching the old soldiers greeting one another after decades of separation, he wondered, why not assemble the veterans of the blocking force so that each would know what the others did—and why—on the mission in Laos? Some had read after-action reports, but most hadn't. Hell, Mike Schaefer played a part in that operation and left the Army without knowing the whole story. Others had heard bits and pieces—some true, some not, some more or less correct but without context. After the mission the survivors scattered to the winds on new tasks and assignments. Some left the Army. Pietro was the link connecting field operators and the staffs in Saigon, Hawaii, and DC. And Jack Plunkett was here. He was the one talking to Pietro and the White House.

Pietro wanted to review a shared experience among old soldiers who might not meet again. Nothing formal. It was personal loyalty to Fat Albert and men like him, some of them in this room. No one in this crowd wanted to embarrass the United States. Everyone had done what he had to do. It was done, finished, closed. It's a long time ago. Shit, it hadn't happened. It remains classified.

The U.S. never acknowledged SOG missions. Vague references and some fragments leaked, but no official history had been written. Media interest ceased when U.S. troops pulled out. Since the fall of the Saigon regime in 1975, the country chose to forget Vietnam, a bad dream. Couldn't forget it fast enough. But some true believers saw the SOG story as a recruiter's dream: The kid who joins the marines or the paratroopers is the kind who responds to the proud story of the recon men. Details were still classified Top Secret by a rigid bureaucracy of mindless minions unable to distinguish a homer from a pop-up. Quill pushers prevail. Can't distinguish between John Wayne posing and heroism. The reflexive desire to guard old secrets dominated. It was just too easy to say "That's classified."

That reality collided with a desire to tell America about real soldiers. Why allow the American people to believe they had an expensive and incompetent military? Dumb! From the war in Vietnam until Desert Storm/Desert Shield, Americans were inclined to think its soldiers were inept. Does anybody think the U.S. Armed Forces were transformed from incompetents to dragon slayers on the weekend before Desert Storm? No. The Army fixed itself. The inspirational SOG story is in folders in gray safes in the Pentagon, behind green doors. The story needs telling! In his fantasies he often saw himself punching out Secretaries, Assistant Secretaries, Deputy Assistant Secretaries, frauds, finks and dipshits. Better said:

Stick close to your desks and never go to sea,

And you all may be Rulers of the Queen's Navee.

***

He chuckled at his indignation and resort to Gilbert and Sullivan. "Next thing you know I'll be singing My Way a la Sinatra. Well, maybe this is the time and place to lay it all out, at least for us at this reunion, before we die with our secrets." But he didn't want the story told in the profane, boozy hubbub of the hospitality room filled with drunks and noise. No one needed a war-story competition for who had the biggest balls. He wanted a quiet place for serious review and reflection.

The idea was to let the men who were on the ground know what had been decided in the head sheds and for staffers to hear just what happened on the ground in the last hours of the operation. Pietro's craving for wholeness was influenced by intimations of mortality. It was time to get it out. Key guys might never muster again. Each year the Special Operations Association roster was shorter by several names.

In the course of the evening Pietro quietly invited the players to an anteroom for a nightcap and a review of the events that took the lives of some friends. The gentle invitation to be with the old man at midnight for a mission recap was understood for what it was: an order.

CHAPTER SIXTEEN

The Telling

Pietro

Mac the Leprechaun arrived first with a bottle of Irish whiskey. It seemed the right thing to do. He and Day had drained a few in Kontum. After the others arrived and settled in, Pietro took the lead.

"It's thirty years since the CCC blocking force was overrun. We each have recollections of our own piece of the action. Some of us have compared notes over the years, but none of us has the whole story. I thought it was time to get it out.

"It begins at my headquarters, Op 35. Then, Rad tells the CCC part. Then, Mike and how Montana saw it. Pete and his time in the bag and what he remembers from the hill. Ken was with Day when he went down, so he probably had the best appreciation of actions on the hill. Jack Plunkett was at JCS and close to our man in the White House. He'll tell us some bad stuff we couldn't know out in the boonies and haven't heard yet. Mark Burns died last year. It would have been good to hear his take on CINCPAC, but the essential red thread goes from Washington to Saigon to Kontum to Dak To and to Major Day in Laos."

Plunkett validated Pietro's point:

"Right. But note that Burns and CINCPAC were with us all the way. No disrespect intended, but Honolulu input isn't important to the mission termination. Once the President had the admiral's concurrence for the operation, the White House gave us a go."

Pietro continued.

"Fat Albert found the choke point in Laos. My brain trust—the Prairie Fire and Salem House desk officers and Jerry Conway, my ops NCO, conceived the operation. Washington was hot for getting out of Vietnam. We wanted to give the enemy a kick in the ass, slow his resupply in the south, and give ARVN a shot at survival. We connected the operation to our government's objective. Interdiction of the enemy main supply route in Laos would contribute to Vietnamization. U.S. troops could come out faster. Mark, in Hawaii and Jack, in DC got the heavy hitters to buy into our concept. We got a 'go.' I gave the order to CCC. Rad?"

Radich

Radich cleared his throat.

"I was pleased. Albert found the choke point and we'd act. I assumed I'd be task force commander, but Colonel Pietro had other ideas. I still get angry when I think of it, but he was probably right.

"I picked the commander, but it couldn't be me. Day was my choice, the right choice. The mission lit up the AO like a Christmas tree. Ridgerunner used air for a big kill and got his team out. Robbie also gets a big kill. But he goes down. Joe Waldron stings the enemy in a classic ambush. But he goes down. The NVA is surprised. They piecemeal, and our guys eat 'em up. As they get their shit in order, Day hurts them in their assembly areas using air. They come at him with tanks and infantry, and our guys wax 'em. The weather closes in. Colonel Pietro and I are at Dak To. He tells me to get 'em out soonest."

Radich stops and glances at Pietro:

"The guys in the field should take it from here."

"Right. Mike, Montana's out there on the trail monitoring traffic."

Mike

Mike Schaefer squinted like a man looking beyond the horizon. Years fell away.

"Montana went in heavy, a Hatchet Team looking for contact, not recon. Infil is unopposed. Probably unobserved. We lay up in thick bush until the Major gives us the code word to execute. We whack a column of bearers and bicycles, killing eleven enemy. No friendly casualties. We move out. No pursuit. That was a surprise, but about this time Covey is working Ridgerunner's target. Then Robbie's. I figure the enemy is too busy to run us down. He doesn't know which way to turn.

"Covey reports initial success at the blocking position on the hill. Joe jumps an enemy column and kills a bunch. I knew from radio traffic that Shadow tore up the enemy at night, and the Major used beaucoup air strikes during the day. Then the weather goes as bad as I've ever seen it. Covey reports the big fight on the hill. I'm too far away to help. The Major and the guys on the hill are overrun. Montana hunkers down wet and miserable for two days. Covey says we need to escape and evade back to Vietnam. I ask for clarification. It was Carpenter as Covey. He repeats the message: E&E to RVN. Extraction in RVN. I don't get it, but I do it. Carpenter always had his shit together."

Mike pauses.

In the pause, Pietro asks:

"When were you given the reason for the failure to extract?"

"In the debrief. They said it was weather. Of course I was pissed when we were out there, but I knew there was a lot going on. I assumed some teams might be worse off, maybe carrying wounded. Maybe on the run. And then the hill was overrun, and I figured people were trying to E&E out. As usual, just attending to the business at hand took all my attention. In RON at night I'd wonder what the hell was going on. In the past, when I asked for extraction, I got it right away. I smelled a rat, but I didn't say that to the team. I said it was the weather and that the other teams were in trouble."

"Mike, what went through your mind when Covey essentially told you to walk to Vietnam?"

"Nothing much, Colonel, beside discomfort, fatigue, and hunger. The usual. I didn't want to get careless, so we made slow progress. We were all at least a little sick from being wet and cold for a few days. A couple of nights it was more like Illinois in November than Vietnam. The cold and our low grade fevers kept our teeth chattering. No contacts. After five days of humping—making it a total of eight days from insertion—we and Covey agreed that we were in RVN. Extraction was uneventful."

"Your debriefers are here," said Roger.

The Leprechaun reported.

"I debriefed. Colonel Radich sat in."

"I remember telling Mike why he had to walk to RVN," said Radich.

"I made a false assumption," said Mike. "I assumed the prohibition on cross border ops came after the hill was overrun. I couldn't imagine a decision to desert the men who were over the fence."

"None of us could," said Pietro. "More on that later. Jack has something to tell us about the infamous order. But first the activity in Laos. We have two eyewitnesses of actions on the hill. Pete Schell was XO of the Exploitation Company, and Ken Key was Day's right-hand man. Pete."

Prisoners of War

Peter Schell was a tall slim man with glasses that added to his professorial image. Fair enough. Pete was a professor of history at a college in Iowa and had been a brave junior officer.

"I was in a fighting bunker with the 1st Platoon on the north side. That was the 12 o'clock from Major Day's perspective, and that's what we called it. The 1st Platoon gave the NVA a lot of grief. The initial contacts were out there, and Spooky/Shadow-type gunships ripped the enemy. When the ground assault came in the heavy rain with tanks, the 1st Platoon stopped the tanks. I think our anti-tank weapons were a great surprise. Then the machine guns and mortars killed a lot of people. There was a break in the action for 10 or 20 minutes. Then the blood really flowed. They kept coming. We kept killing them. They wanted us off that hill.

"Our machine guns were very effective. I don't know how common it was, but I saw an NVA leader shoot one of his soldiers who stopped advancing. For them, facing us was probable death. Failure to attack was certain death. And the mortars were right on them. There were some very brave enemy troops in that assault. And impressive discipline.

"I was busy, so I'm not aware of what happened in other sectors of the hill. I remember that at one point I checked my ammo pockets and found two full magazines. With the one in my weapon, that was three. I started with 20. I had fired up 17 magazines of 28 rounds each."

Pete took off his glasses and wiped them with a tissue from his pocket. Then he went on.

"The Major was smart to load up to the north. The enemy paid a great price.

"I lost all sense of time. I have images of NVA troops suddenly visible at five or ten meters as they moved toward me in the rain. I fired. They fell. Others came out of the rain. Flares from the mortars lit 'em up. The rain, flares and enemy faces and battle noise made a surrealistic scene. I had the sensation of being in a film. I shot a lot of people.

"After checking my ammo, I heard a loud boom, maybe a concussion grenade. The next thing I saw was enemy troops around me. My head hurt, but I registered what they were doing as I woke up. They were shooting the Montagnards and badly wounded U.S. I think they wanted American POWs who could walk. They were all around me. I remember wondering if they had the whole hill or just some of it.

"They got me standing and tied my hands behind my back. They must have stripped me of my web gear when I was stunned. Anyway, I was pushed, not a mean push. More like a signal. A nudge. My head hurt like hell. They were telling me to move out. I did.

"The rain was heavy. It was dark. We slid and tripped in mud, in barbed wire, in shell holes. Feeling sorry for myself, I realized that they couldn't see any better than I could. And they were close to exhaustion from the approach march, the assault, and now this. So I broke away and moved in a direction I believed to be east. I just kept bashing in the bush. Maybe they came after me. Maybe they were too beat to care. I just don't know.

"When I couldn't hear voices or gunshots, I stopped to work off the rope they'd secured my hands with. Then I went into the thickest stuff in the area. I was miserable, and I was alone. I focused on two notions. They couldn't track me in the rain; at sun-up I'd find out where east was.

"God, it was cold.

"In the morning I headed east. A week later I stumbled onto an LZ where a bird picked me up. They tell me I flashed a signal, but I have no recollection of that. I remember walking toward the sunrise, and I remember having some pocket items on that first day. The NVA must have been too scared or too busy to do a thorough body search on the hill.

"I had a metal mirror, salted nuts, hard candy, morphine, malaria tablets, pep pills, and a bottle of cough medicine stuffed in various pockets. I always did that. We learned that in Germany on field exercises with the 10th SF Group: always carry pocket items in case you gotta run. In the hospital they told me I had only morphine and the clothing I wore when I was admitted. I guess I was on automatic pilot and consumed the other stuff. I was delirious, according to the doctor who treated me.

"Later some exotic diseases showed up: Blackwater Fever, Dengue, and the famous FOUO—fever of unknown origin. They got me filled up with fluids and packed me off to Letterman Army Hospital. I was close to both rotation from Vietnam and discharge from the Army, so a few weeks later I was released from the hospital. Then I was released from the Army. They kept me on active duty until I recovered.

"I want to add something.

"Veteran organizations, like VFW, American Legion and DAV, and civic organizations like Rotary, and church groups ask me to speak. People know me as the guy who was a POW and escaped.

"I was a prisoner for a few minutes. That's important. We were always told in training that your chances for escape were better sooner rather than later. Battlefield confusion and being in the hands of combat troops, not police or professional prisoner chasers, gives a guy chances to escape. I remembered that and took the first one. So, pass the word to the troops still doing the job: if taken POW, make your play to escape ASAP. Things only get worse.

"One more point. I want to thank Colonel Pietro, Colonel Radich, and all the others who didn't give up on us, even after a week. That bird that took me out was there because you put it there. You could have assumed that after so much time there were no survivors, but you kept the faith. You always did, and we knew it."

**

They were quiet. Each of them imagined himself in shock, dazed from the concussion, wet, cold, sick, miserable, alone, and a long way from home: a week in dense jungle in a denied area putting one foot after the other as he followed sunrise. And we give prizes for running a Marathon. Each person in the room asked if he could have done what Pete did. Most men would sit down and die. Give up. What would I have done?

Pete was one brave historian.

Pietro spoke for all of them:

"Pete, I wish that I had half your guts and determination."

There was an assenting murmur.

Pietro went on.

"We searched for survivors for a month. Eventually two U.S. and 12 Yards made it back. The Yards walked back to Vietnam and kept walking. They were afraid if they revealed themselves to a chopper they might be gunned down as VC or NVA. Both Americans got signals up to aircraft and got rides back from the border area.

"We had several false alarms, either radio or transponder signals. We followed up but failed to make contact. It might have been the enemy fooling with captured gear. Maybe they wanted to sucker us in. But just maybe it was one of ours—sick, wounded, on the run, hoping for a miracle."

He paused, thinking and turned to the former CCC commander.

"I remember Colonel Radich saying that the hardest thing he ever did in uniform was to order an end to the search after a month."

Radich got teary-eyed and said:

"I think of it often. The thought of one of ours wandering ... abandoned."

His voice drifted off.

Pietro spoke.

"We have another tough old soldier here, Sergeant Major Ken Key, USA, retired. Ken was Day's alter ego on the hill and at CCC. I always thought we could have done a training film showing the two of them at work. We could show it to junior officers and NCOs as a kind of 'how to work with one another,' or something similar.

"Ken, tell us about the end of the mission."

"Yes, sir. First, thanks for what you just said. It's true. From the beginning I liked him, and I know he liked me. We all had the feeling that he really cared for us. You may not know it, but he packed off his first NCOIC, a rigid guy and a real nervous Nelly. The Major told the man to find a home where he'd like to work. No hard feelings. We just can't work together. The guy found a home. No fuss, no bother. Then the Major called me in and said, 'Uncle Ken, run it.' And I did. He called me his daddy rabbit.

"He wanted mission-type orders, and he gave mission-type orders. His exact words—I heard them often enough to remember exactly: 'Tell me the outcome you want; then get out of the way.' He practiced what he preached. He'd say, 'Uncle Ken, I want this to happen. Can you do it?' If I said yes, he'd get out of my way. If I said no, he'd ask how we might handle it. But I never had any doubt about what he wanted. He'd ask, 'Is that crazy talk?' If I said yes, he might drop it. But that was the way he got me and the others involved. He said life is full of surprises, but let's not surprise one another. If one of us had a bright idea or a hair up his ass, we'd talk it over with the Major.

"We'd work 12-14 hour days and think we were having fun. We actually watched one another carefully. If a guy got tired and made mistakes, sometimes the man wouldn't know it. I'd go to the Major and say so-and-so needs a stand down. He'd say, do it, and I'd tell the guy to get his ass to Nha Trang or Saigon for a few days.

"You're right. We shoulda made a training film on how officers and NCOs should work together.

"One day I went to his office and closed the door—a couple of boards from an ammo box. He said, 'Oh-oh, Uncle Ken. Am I in trouble?' I said, 'Take a stand down. Go to Nha Trang.' He said, 'Why?' 'Cuz you're fucked up,' I said. He looked at me to see if I was joking, saw I was serious, and took a few days off. That should be in the training film. That's about trust. He trusted my judgment.

"When the Colonel Radich told him he'd be Task Force Commander, I told him he wasn't going without me. He just said, 'Of course. I know that. We go together.'"

Key stared ahead and spoke very deliberately.

"I'll pick it up with the final assault. We knew that we hurt the enemy real bad. Air tore him up again and again. First, Grady with the night gunships at OP-1. God, what a show that was! They were surprised. Caught in the open. Paid a very high price. Then Ridgerunner and Robbie on the trail flat brought pee on 'em. And Joe's ambush. Then the tank attack on our hill. The 57mm reckless rifles did a hell of a job. That got their attention. Probably figured tanks would shock us and lower the boom. Finish us, as we were ineffective with our little popguns.

"It was going all our way even when the weather closed in. Never saw anything like that rain and shit for visibility in five years in that part of the world. We had no doubt what that meant. Without air, we could make it expensive for the NVA, but if he was prepared to pay the price, he could take us.

"As soon as we had our first contact and Ridgerunner had his, the Major said he had good news and bad news. The good news was that we had the enemy by the balls. The bad news was that we had enemy by the balls. Ya didn't hafta be a Leavenworth genius to realize that the NVA had to open the trail. He'd do what he had to do.

"I was standing next to Major Day when he talked to the CCC commander and the S-4 that last time from our command bunker on the hill. He never blew smoke up the chain, and he didn't bullshit the troops. No pep talk. He just made me feel—and I think most of the guys—that whatever was coming down, we'd stick together. That made it all right.

"When he put down the handset and grabbed his weapon, I

grabbed mine. The situation called for trigger pullers, so we became riflemen. He headed for the heaviest fire, and I followed him. There was action in every direction, from the sounds of it. The artillery calls it a target rich environment. Shit, it was so rich that we coulda found targets to butt stroke. We went slip-slidin' around. Couldn't see shit. Even with the 81s popping illum, you know how shadows do tricks as the flare 'chutes wobble. Had to sort the shadows and bushes from bad guys, all of 'em jumping around. Then ya had to sort the good folks from the bad folks. Like Pete said, it was a strange movie. Maybe more a bad dream.

"The Major looked back to see if I'm OK. He points to a firefight ahead, and I knew he meant that we might just as well jump in right there. And we did. Like Pete said, they had balls, those NVA. I didn't count magazines, but I had it on go-go all the time. In the fog and all it was like one of them Frankenstein movies. All of a sudden I'd see bad guys steppin' outa the rain and ground haze, an' I'd hose 'em. The other guys were doin' the same thing, and the NVA was doin' it to us. AKs and B-40, M-60s and CAR-15s, illumination and rain. It was like a World War I film.

"Off to the right the fire was loudest, and I figured that was maybe a breakthrough. The Major must've thought so, cuz he catches my eye and points over that way. We slide over there in the muck and they're all mixed up. I mean, there was no line of contact. It was more like a barroom brawl with CAR-15s and AKs. All the time the 81s are pumping out HE, Willie Pete, and illumination rounds. The 57s aren't perfect for that kinda work, but the gunners are usin' up their ammo and tearing up enemy troops. Shit, couldn't miss!

"Where we are, in the middle of this fight with everybody mixed up, the danger to my mind was me blowin' away a Yard or an American— or some friendly blowin' me away. I'm really wiped out an' goin' on adrenaline. I was popping an empty magazine out to reload when a mean little bastard is about to push a bayonet my way. The Major uses his weapon like a ball bat upside the mean bastard's head. I pop a fresh mag in my weapon, and I see an NVA empty a magazine into the Major. I kill the NVA, and check the Major. No pulse. He's already dead. He's hit, hell, 10-12 times—chest, abdomen, neck, and face. I put my thumb on his carotid. Nothing! I check for pulse on his wrist. Nothing. I check the big artery inside his thigh. Nothing."

The old soldier paused to sip some Irish whiskey and compose himself. His voice had gotten soft, harsh, and slow. The sip speeded it up and made it a little louder.

"He was dead. I go back to work, and I don't know how long. I got a blow to the head. I figured an NVA pole axed me, but later I find out it was a crease from a gunshot. I'm out for I don't know how long—this phase is kind of a blur. When I come to, an enemy soldier is wrapping my head with the bandage from my first aid pack. I told you they were good. Must've done his basic at Fort Benning, or Dix, or Jackson.

"Like with Pete, they finish off all the Yards and U.S. who are bad hurt. They wanted American POWs, but only if they were ambulatory. I wish I had Pete's good sense, but I was fucked up in my head. He's right. Best to break for it right away.

"I was a POW for about 24 hours, I think, before I broke away. From the hill they took me to a kind of a rest area. Let me tell you we dinged 'em! I was with a bunch of wounded NVA. They thought I was worse off than I was. Must have been all the blood on my face and head. Maybe my natural ugly. Anyway, no cage for me. I think that's coming when they see I'm OK, so I decide to haul ass soon's I can.

"They got me half-assed tied, but I work out of the knots. Security is lax, which surprises me. Later I realize they're bushed, much worse off than me. Think about it. Ducking U.S. air, long marches, assault up a hill into heavy fire, rain and cold. We always see it from our side. Them poor pricks went through a helluva week and then we killed them in the rain and mud, most of them sick and miserable. Even blew up their tanks. All they could expect was to lay up, get a little rest, and then do it all again.

"Anyways, I walk outa there so easy I can't believe it. All the stories I heard and read about our POWs who got away made it sound much harder than I found it.

"We'd crossed an east flowin' blue line the day before. No doubt in my mind where I'm headin', or how. My personal E&E plan was to get in some driftwood goin' the right way, an' that's just what I do. The next day I lay up after a very careful exit from that stream. Next night I'm back in my favorite stream leavin' the drivin' to it and that driftwood. The second day I lay up again, but I head for where I saw the sunrise. After five days I flag down a chopper by wavin' my shirt and showin' my lily white ass."

Pietro, who had read Ken's after action report, asked, for the benefit of those who hadn't:

"Pete had pocket items for survival, and you didn't. How did you make it without food, medicine, a mirror, etc.?"

"Well, sir, first it was pure fear. I knew about being a POW. No way I was gonna rot in the jungle in a cage, and a few years in the Hanoi Hilton didn't sound good either. Better off dead, I figured. About the food. I ran a lot of E&E problems in Okie and around Asia on mobile training team missions. I know a man can go without food for a week, and I know a man must have water. So I drank water every chance I got. My weight before the mission was 160. When the medics weighed me after my rescue I was 'round 130. Maybe another couple of days woulda done me in. Kinda glad I didn't find out. Missing water woulda done me in, but I had lots of water."

Quiet settled on the group. Then Pietro spoke.

"Powerful stuff, Ken. Without getting preachy, you and Pete make two obvious training points. First, over the years you got some good E&E and survival training. Two, you and Pete are determined men. All of us were proud to serve with you two and the others on that mission.

"Now I'd like to ask Jack to put us in the picture. What happened in Washington, especially at the end?"

Reaction in Washington

Jack Plunkett chose his words carefully and spoke slowly.

"You know that I was in on the mission from the beginning. The concept was hatched from the Fat Albert debrief. Everyone in the special ops community—who was aware of it—thought it fit perfectly into what political authority wanted to happen: get the U.S. out; turn the war over to the Vietnamese.

"I'll try to give you the feel of things in DC after PJ Riley broke the story in print and blew SOG's cover.

"First, though, hearing you this evening beats the hell out of my recollections of the after-action reports, now so long ago. No matter how hard we try to get it straight, stories become distorted unless we get them the way you guys did in your debriefs: before men compare notes and confuse facts with opinions. Before showers and hot chow. Give a human being time and he'll produce a plausible story rather than a true story, even if he tries to tell the true story. A British general put it something like this: on the day of battle the naked truth can be had for the asking; the next day the truth puts on its uniform.

"Political authority in DC bought off on your operation so that we could speed up Vietnamization. At the time, the anti-war movement was also in full bloom. Slowing enemy logistics to the south fit political intent perfectly. From the beginning we understood that we had to give the President plausible deniability. By 1970 the SOG mission was some seven years old, and while the press had reported some parts of it, no one had put the whole thing together. We hoped to pull off the mission secretly.

"The Riley story took us by surprise. Colonel Pietro warned me, but until it actually appeared we'd hoped that the Times editors would hold it for a day or two, until we could get our people out of Laos. But they had a big story. They intended to get it out before the competition got it and printed it.

"That decision was topped by nervous twits in the White House. Karl assumed that termination of operations over the fence meant after we got our blocking force and RTs out. We got that wrong. They meant no more ops in Laos. Period. Karl called me, told me, and quit his job. He was angry, indignant, outraged. He couldn't believe that American civilian leadership could literally desert American soldiers. The last time I was with him he was pissed, but he showed his usual cool and rational self. I had no idea what was coming.

"Karl Berenson was as decent as he was smart. Maybe that explains it. I suspect most of you read about him in the flurry of newspaper and weekly magazine pieces and the TV stories. I knew him well. The press was right about him. He was the best and the brightest that this country produces. I was shocked. What he did was medieval.

261

"In his suicide note he said that the SOG mission was his creature. He said neither the President nor his National Security Counselor knew about SOG. The White House thought it really was a Studies and Observation Group, an intel think tank in-country. Karl took the fall. No one asked him to take responsibility, but he did. He said that the military believed he was speaking for the President; the President said that he had complete confidence in Colonel Berenson. So, it was made to look like a White House basement operation run by an Army colonel. No matter that not everyone bought it. It was plausible deniability. It gave the White House some cover. Executive immunity took care of the rest until the Watergate mess. Then the President got his. But the SOG story remained buried. Amazing. Think of it: petty burglary—house breaking—did in the President of the United States when violation of international law, deceiving the Congress and the American people, and betraying his soldiers couldn't do him in.

"I can understand Karl's suicide this way: his sense of honor was somehow conflated with his desire to save the Office of the President. The press said he was ashamed of what he did. Not so. He was proud of what he did. But he was ashamed that his mentor and the President, the man we respect as Commander-in-Chief, could write off American soldiers in Laos. He could square a circle by killing himself while leaving a note that absolved all others. So that's what he did. His personal code of honor was beyond the comprehension of the crowd he had served, the best and the brightest.

"He overdosed on honor."

Pietro

The room went silent before Pietro spoke.

"So, how do we end this story?

"Brave men gave all for a 'successful' mission. Successful because it killed a lot of enemy troops and broke a lot of enemy things? Then how come Saigon is now called Ho Chi Minh City? Because our government betrayed our soldiers? Successful because a man like Karl died to protect lesser men? Successful because PJ Riley became a career journalist over the dead bodies of his friends? Successful, because newspapers claim

First Amendment to sell advertising space? Successful because chicken hawks who ducked their war can wrap themselves in the flag and mutter their greasy patriotic platitudes to get themselves elected?"

Mike Schaefer spoke.

"Colonel, you ask, 'How do we end this story?' I'll take a shot at that.

"I can't address all the questions you raise, even to my own satisfaction, but I do see more cause for satisfaction than you do.

"First, PJ. We should value the press not for the good it does but for the evil it prevents. He did what he did well, and I think he believes he did the right thing. Others may believe it was ambition, but I don't. His crime was tracking the truth and reporting it. We mourn the loss of friends and see it differently.

"Second, Colonel Berenson took his life out of a sense of honor and to protect and defend the reputation of the United States of America. The men in this room have demonstrated that they were proud to die for—not to talk about—what they shared with him: duty, honor, country.

"Third, Hanoi. Hanoi won because it wanted Saigon more than Washington wanted Saigon and more than Saigon wanted Saigon. My hat's off to them.

"Fourth, Special Operations today. My son is in law school right now, but his pre-law course was Desert Storm as a Special Forces sergeant. The story doesn't end. Recently two of ours were awarded Medals of Honor for doing all they could do to keep the faith with another American soldier. They died for a fellow soldier. That's our tradition.

"Finally, about the men we were privileged to call friends.

"I propose a toast to Fat Albert, Grady, Robbie, Joe, the Mad Major, and the others who gave us more than we deserve."

"And to those now serving who continue the mission," said Ken Key.

"God bless the United States of America," said Mac.

They drank to their friends and country.

It was about the men.

Boston

Saturday night, 10 p.m., a man on the Boston Globe's foreign desk is working. Out of the corner of his eye he sees another man having a sandwich for his lunch while looking at the Sunday paper the printers have just sent up. The ink is drying, giving off a unique soybean fragrance.

"Anything good in the Sunday paper?"

"Nah, same-o same-o. Sox lost. And PJ going on about his old war."

He rolls his sandwich wrapper into a ball, launches it as a basketball one-hander, and announces, "Two points" as his ball sinks into a wastebasket.

About the Author

Henry G. Gole, Colonel, USA, Ret., was an enlisted infantryman in the Korean War and a Special Forces officer in two combat tours in Viet Nam. His doctorate is from Temple University. He has taught at several institutions of higher learning. In addition to numerous articles and book reviews, his four published books are: *Exposing the Third Reich, Colonel Truman Smith in Hitler's Germany* (2013); *General William E. DePuy, Preparing the Army for Modern War* (2008); *Soldiering: Observations from Korea, Viet Nam, and Safe Places* (2005); and *The Road to Rainbow: Army Planning for Global War, 1934-1940* (2003).

Made in United States
Orlando, FL
17 January 2024

42612014R00161